Contents

Acknowledgements

The Health Education Authority is indebted to the following individuals:

The Healthy Colleges Project

Project co-ordinator   Terry O'Donnell
Continuing Education Division

Assistant co-ordinator   Judy Taylor
Birmingham Education Department

Link lecturers   Mike Allderidge ⎫ Brooklyn College,
Teresa Ibberson ⎭ Birmingham
Mary Clayburn
East Birmingham College

Secretarial staff   Val Busby
Viv Madden

Advisory committee   David Bradbury, Jackie Brerton, Robin Doughty, Lynda Finn, Diana Harrap, Peggy Harris, Geoff Hyde, Val Little, John Lloyd, Julian McCormick, Lindsay Neil, Andrea Rivlin, David Toeman, David Williets

Health in Further Education Project:
Case Studies of Colleges

Project team   Gay Gray
Ann Payne ⎫ Tailor
Heather Hyde ⎬ Made
Derek Close ⎭ Training

Secretary   Elizabeth Longland

Advisory committee   Lynda Finn, Ruth Joyce, Paul Hayton, Faith Hill, Stuart McKoy, Maurice Mealing, Derek Powell, Danielle Wayne

Text of Part I edited and revised by Mavis Gregson

The publishers are grateful for permission to reproduce the following copyright material:

Figure 2: adapted from A. Beattie 'A structural repertoire of the model of health education' at a Health Education Certificate Tutors' Workshop, March 1980 and A. Beattie 'Community development for health: from practice to theory?', *Radical Health Promotion*, issue 4, 1986.
Figure 7: adapted from J. Ryder and L. Campbell *Balancing Acts in Personal, Social and Health Education* (Routledge, 1988).

Abbreviations used in this report

BTEC	Business and Technology Education Council
CPVE	Certificate of Pre-vocational Education
DES	Department of Education and Science (now DFE: Department for Education)
DH	Department of Health
DHA	District Health Authority
FE	Further Education
FEU	Further Education Unit
GNVQs	General National Vocational Qualifications
HEA	Health Education Authority
LAA	Local Authorities Association
MAFF	Ministry of Agriculture, Fisheries and Food
NRA	National Record of Achievement
NVQs	National Vocational Qualifications (and SVQs: Scottish Vocational Qualifications)
TVEI	Technical and Vocational Education Initiative
WHO	World Health Organisation
YTS	now YT: Youth Training

Introduction

Since April 1988 the Health Education Authority has provided support on the theme of the health-promoting college to a number of further education colleges. This publication presents the findings from the support provided. In the light of the Government's White Paper *The Health of the Nation* (DH, 1992) which outlines a strategy for health in England, *The Health-promoting College* offers practical information for colleges, and for all concerned with post-16 education and training, on the contributions they can make to the attainment of the White Paper's targets.

The Health-promoting College is divided into two parts. The first part is based on work funded by the Health Education Authority, together with the Further Education Unit, West Midlands Regional Health Authority, South Birmingham Health Authority and Birmingham Education Department, which took place in Birmingham between April 1988 and July 1989. Based on practical experience, it examines health education at policy and institutional level, with a specific emphasis on developing a whole college approach to health promotion. A variety of institutional, curriculum and staff development approaches is illustrated, through examples that focus on health areas which link directly with the targets identified in *The Health of the Nation*.

The second part also explores opportunities for health promotion in further education in a practical manner, through case study reports on Health Education Authority initiatives in seventeen colleges, from April 1990 to March 1991. Furthermore, it usefully reflects on the actual process of change itself. A number of issues recur. The importance of commitment from senior managers is one, and the allocation of resources to back up this commitment is another.

The intended audience for *The Health-promoting College* is senior college executives. Readers will find that the report contains both practical advice and thoughtful reflection on health education and health promotion. It is increasingly recognised that health issues have a direct bearing on both the efficiency and the effectiveness of any organisation. This is particularly true of large institutions, such as colleges. Following college incorporation in April 1993, health issues associated with human resource development and occupational health, for both students and staff, have come into very sharp focus. According to *Education and Training for the 21st Century*, vol. 2 (DES, 1991), the colleges to be given new independent management cater for almost two million students. Their potential impact on the nation's health is clearly a considerable one.

The Health-promoting College makes it plain that those advancing health education initiatives must demonstrate to management the way these link directly to the developmental priorities of the college. Long-term strategies and policies are needed, to provide structures and mechanisms supporting the process of change. So as not to overwhelm staff, it is important that change is carefully piloted, and that it integrates health education with other overlapping curriculum developments currently taking place in further education, choosing particularly those which are national priorities. With the backing of the White Paper, the current spate of change in further education does in fact offer a positive opportunity to place both health education, and the active learning strategies through which it is best achieved, high on college agendas.

The healthy colleges project   1

The project in outline   1

Background

During the past decade, it has been recognised that attention to
health matters in the post-16 education sector has been largely
non-existent. Yet this is at a time when colleges have become
increasingly populated by young people and older adults whose
school careers may not have included a planned and co-
ordinated programme of health education. Over the same
period there has been increasing emphasis on the important
role of schools in making children aware of both their own and
the community's health needs. Bodies such as the Department
of Health (DH), the Department for Education (DFE) and the
Health Education Authority (HEA) have contributed to this
view. However, in the post-16 sector, nothing comparable has
taken place.

   It was within this context that the action research project,
Health Promotion and Health Education in Colleges of Further
Education, was developed. The project, which ran from April
1988 to July 1989, was designed to address the development of
a policy and strategy for health promotion and health education
in the post-16 sector. Through its range of funding sources, the
HEA, the Further Education Unit (FEU), the West Midlands
Regional Health Authority, South Birmingham Health
Authority and the City of Birmingham Education Department,
the project secured a national and regional profile, in addition
to its local base.

The project partners

Project pilot activity was predominantly based in one college,
Bournville College of Further Education. To provide a contrast

of environment and curriculum, two associate colleges, Brooklyn College and East Birmingham College, were also involved. Between them the curriculum of the three colleges was broadly representative of FE. All three colleges were general rather than specialist in character, and had multi-ethnic student bodies including both adults and 16- to 19-year-olds. Bournville College served a varied local community and drew students from across the city of Birmingham, including significant numbers of young people from inner city districts. In April 1988 it had a student population in the region of 4000, evenly divided between 16–19 and post-19 groups, 55 per cent male and 45 per cent female, with approximately 37 per cent of ethnic minority origin.

Aim of the project

The main aim of the project was to develop a policy and strategy for health promotion and health education in Birmingham's colleges of further education by:

- planning and implementing a college-based project which explores and exploits the advantages of a 'whole college' approach
- recording and analysing the progress achieved and processes involved in the conduct and delivery of the pilot project
- designing an appropriate and effective dissemination programme, suitable for implementation locally and nationally.

Terminology and guiding principles

The project proposal clarified the terms 'health promotion' and 'health education'. Health promotion seeks to enable people to increase control over and to improve their health. It subsumes health education, that is, learning opportunities which can help individuals to make choices about their health. It is recognised that health education is the most important process by which health promotion objectives can be achieved.

In seeking to develop the policy, seven guiding principles were identified in the project submission. It was proposed that the project should:

- involve the college population as a whole and not simply focus on people 'at risk'
- seek support and participation as widely as possible and at all levels within the college
- direct its attention to *all* potential determinants of health in the college environment, in its curriculum, and in the area of staff–student relationships
- ensure that project activities encourage a variety of approaches, compatible and co-ordinated with other related initiatives
- be prepared to take advantage of any available resources or expertise in the community which can contribute to project aims
- seek to create and sustain lasting support networks in the community in order to sustain the ongoing impact of project outcomes
- develop proposals which take account of the need for continuity, pre-16 and post-college.

Intended outcomes

Within the pilot college, intended outcomes were to include:

- the definition and adoption of a policy which recognises its role as a health-promoting institution
- progress towards establishing a college environment and curricula which are consistently conducive to positive health
- more positive health behaviour among staff and students at an individual level, and by strengthening of networks within the college which can contribute to this end.

Within and beyond the pilot college, intended outcomes were to include:

- a report suitable for dissemination to all colleges in Birmingham and to other institutions of FE throughout England and Wales
- proposals for dissemination of project findings, including those relating to processes involved
- identification of policy priorities and of ongoing

resources required for their implementation, in order to encourage and extend good practice in Birmingham beyond the pilot college

- recommendations for further action.

Method of approach

As directed, the project took a whole college approach. It focused attention on all potential health determinants within the institution. It used a framework of four key, inter-related institutional determinants:

- *institution:* the organisational practices, ethos and culture
- *environment:* the physical setting and services
- *curriculum*
- *staff–student relationships.*

As its value base, the project approach was based on three explicit assumptions:

- the college and its environment can and does exercise both positive and negative influences on health
- curriculum can be modified to accommodate health promotion and health education by integration into mainstream programmes, rather than by bolt-on packages or options
- relationships between staff and students reflect and contribute to the well-being of individuals and the health of the organisation.

Summary of project activities

It was important for project staff to work closely with and be supported by senior managers in the project colleges. A three-day residential conference, 'Managing the Healthy College', was held in December 1988 for the managers of all eight city colleges. This was intended to raise awareness of the concept of the health-promoting college, and to obtain college managers' views.

A combination of data collection methods and research strategies was used throughout the project. These were determined by prevailing circumstances and shifts in perception and action as the project progressed. They included:

- *survey work* to ascertain existing knowledge, views and attitudes
- *observation* of conditions and practices
- unstructured, informal *interviews*
- *direct action* such as:
    training courses
    support groups
    tutoring or co-tutoring sessions within learning
      programmes
    discussion of specific health topics by college
      management teams and other formal college groups.

Strategies for curriculum development were varied and included:

- delivering and organising staff development courses in the project college and in eight further education and four sixth-form colleges
- exploratory and developmental work with course teams
- work with course groups singly or in a co-tutoring format
- liaising with individual staff development tutors
- liaising with the city staff development network (FE)
- working directly with staff and students currently in the FE initial teacher-training scheme.

The quality development team of the city continuing education division provided support to both the curriculum development and to the project work as a whole.

The following aspects of health were addressed by specific health promotion initiatives:

- fitness and health awareness
- the establishment of a no-smoking environment
- healthy food choices
- HIV/AIDS and sexual health education.

Following a Health Awareness Day event, which included displays and fitness testing in all three pilot colleges on a first come-first served basis, fitness testing by appointment was organised for staff by request in two of the colleges. All three colleges sought to establish a no-smoking environment. The methods varied since the colleges were all at different starting points. Research into healthy food choices was conducted with the caterers contracted to city colleges, centred on the main pilot college. Consultation took place on the examination of catering with the personnel of South Birmingham Health Authority and West Midlands Health Authority.

To develop health education on HIV and AIDS, project staff consulted District Health Authority (DHA) staff within Birmingham, and staff from the environmental health services. Training courses and activities with tutorial groups were designed and delivered with the senior health education officer with responsibility for HIV and AIDS in four of Birmingham's five DHAs, two health education officers from South Birmingham Health Authority, and members of Women and Theatre, Birmingham.

The concepts of health promotion and health education   2

Notions of health

The individual context

Currently medical practice tends to define health as the absence of clinically diagnosed diseases or disability. The health of the nation is looked at through statistics showing the incidence of illness, death rates or causes of death. In the same way, the public often thinks that, as long as it does not have an illness with a definite name, it can count itself as healthy. A smoker, for instance, may not see shortness of breath or a morning cough as signs of illness. Someone in late middle age may regard loss of teeth as normal ageing.

A different view of health is to see it as a wider and much more positive concept. This definition of health relates to the whole person and to such aspects of the overall pattern of life as feeling confident to cope, enjoying life and being able to adapt to change. Far more is included than simply the absence of physical or mental disease. An individual's ability to act in a variety of relationships with other people, to experience and cope with a range of emotions, to sustain an inner self supported by core values and beliefs may all enter into this more holistic sense of health and well-being.

The impact of social environment

It is not possible, either, to focus on health as solely a matter for individuals. Whether within the broader or the narrower concept, health cannot be viewed in isolation from the social environments in which individuals' lives and choices are shaped. A succession of reviews on health status have demonstrated the social dimensions of health. For example, applying definitions of health related to presence of disease reveals that there are marked inequalities in distribution by social class, race and gender.

Promoting health and preventing disease

The commitment

If health is defined in a way that takes account of the whole person, it means that the promotion of health includes any activity that enhances positive health and well-being. The World Health Organisation (1984) has defined health promotion as 'the process of enabling people to increase control over, and to improve, their health ... [It] ... involves the population as a whole in the context of their everyday life, rather than focusing on people at risk from specific diseases.' This view of health encompasses not only physical conditions but also personal and social resources. It is central to the WHO (1978) Declaration of Alma-Ata, which directs countries to attain 'Health for All' by the year 2000.

As a signatory to this declaration, the UK has acknowledged that health is both one of the most important products we can create, and one of the most important resources needed to create any other kind of wealth. The view of health adopted by the WHO is usefully summarised in three policy aims:

- to add years to life
- to add health to life
- to add life to years.

The challenge for the future

To achieve these aims the many challenges of preventing illness and promoting good health must be met. People may be living longer but many still die prematurely (before age 65). Others may have the quality of their lives impaired by avoidable ill health. Coronary heart disease (CHD) is both the single largest cause of death, and the single main cause of premature death in England. Although the death rate for CHD in England has been declining since the late 1970s, it remains one of the highest in the world. Other major causes of death and disability include stroke, cancer and accidents. *The Health of the Nation* has identified five key areas in its strategy for health in England: coronary heart disease and stroke, cancers, mental illness, HIV/AIDS and sexual health, and accidents. It is felt that success in these areas would contribute to an improvement in terms of life expectancy and quality of life.

Death and disability are related to our behaviour, lifestyle and work. Statistics show that these in turn are affected by the society in which we live and our access to its resources. In 1980, the government report *Inequalities in Health* (see Townsend and Davidson, eds, 1982), widely known as the Black Report, presented a detailed analysis of health data from the start of the NHS to the early 1970s. While the mortality rates for men and women aged 35 and over had steadily diminished in the higher and intermediate professional groups, semi-skilled and unskilled groups had either improved very little or had deteriorated. This had occurred at all stages of life and was found to be rooted in material deprivation. The report argued that much of the problem lies outside the scope of the NHS, and is more crucially located in social and economic factors, such as income, work and unemployment, education, housing, transport and the environment. Data from the Office of Population, Censuses and Surveys in June 1989 show a substantial and widening gap between the top and bottom occupational groups (Goldblatt, 1989). Whitehead (1987), in a review of health data done to update the Black Report, found that women's health varies in relation to employment, marital status and social class, with the health of working-class women being particularly poor. The patterns of ill health among and between ethnic minority groups show a complex picture, with rates for death and illness varying both by disease and by community. It is clear that effective health care must provide for the specific needs of ethnic minority groups in ways that respect cultural differences.

To improve health on the scale required, curative medicine alone can make relatively little contribution. Health education is one of the most important processes for achieving the objectives of disease prevention and health promotion. The aim must be to prevent illness and promote health by changing both individual and collective behaviour. This must be done by extending and developing the frame of reference in which individuals make their health choices; in other words, through health education.

Approaches to health education

Confused perceptions

The traditional perception of health education is often that of being told to stop doing some things and start doing others 'for your own good'. The messages might be delivered by health professionals. Or they may be delivered by the media whose style of communication has become increasingly sophisticated. In the last decade, however, new approaches to health education have been developing. These are based on increased understanding of the causes of ill health, on a wider concept of health and on a desire to promote well-being. Sometimes these new approaches are complementary to each other; sometimes, however, they are conflicting.

Some strategies aim primarily to change the behaviour of the individual. They seek to promote this by giving information and advice on health risks. Other strategies recognise that, unless provided sensitively, information and advice about health risks may be rejected; and hence that they need to vary the emphasis. For instance, it may be necessary to take into account that there may be no scope for the individual to act upon the information. It may clash with existing knowledge or beliefs. It may be seen as threatening or may appear to be a passing fad.

Some styles of health education are concerned with fostering the skills to assess information and make decisions. Others, which seek to facilitate personal growth, take full account of the client's own experiences and circumstances. Yet others focus on the need to change environments and social conditions in order to create more possibilities for the individual to make healthy choices. 'Social action' approaches such as these use professional expertise and scientific evidence to lobby governments, organisation, and the public at large. The intention is to instigate from above change which will promote rather than detract from health. To enhance 'ownership' of the outcomes of such actions, this may be done by working collectively with communities to pursue the beneficial changes.

A framework for health education

Four models

To assist clarification, approaches to health education can be organised into models with distinctive aims and modes of action. A number of such classifications have been developed. The project drew on several of these when exploring issues in health education with various groups of staff and evolved a four-fold classification for health education:

- the health-risk advice model
- the educational/rational model
- the self-empowerment model
- the action for change model.

Figure 1 presents these models in detail. The project's classification does not mark a radical departure from other available models (Rawson and Grigg, 1988). However, it provides a methodology which shifts the focus of health education away from teacher-centred education (health-risk advice model and educational/rational model) to learner-centred approaches, emphasising the individual needs of the learner (self-empowerment model and action-for-change model).

Fig. 1. Four models

i The health-risk advice model

In this model the purpose of health education is to prevent illness by changing individuals' behaviour. Information and advice is directed at individuals thought to be at risk, or at the population as a whole. Action may be directly coercive; it may try to persuade; or it may take the stance that in the light of the advice given, individuals are free to make their own choices.

The disadvantages of the model is that information-giving may raise awareness, but behaviour change may not follow this up in a rational manner. To be motivated to take preventive action, the individuals receiving the information and advice must:

- be motivated to protect their health
- believe they are at risk from the disease in question and that the consequences will be serious if they do not act
- believe that the recommended action is valid
- consider that the benefits of action outweigh the costs
- be able to consider the above issues and make decisions
- have access to the resources and conditions necessary for action.

ii The educational/rational model

This approach gives information while at the same time providing opportunities for the development of decision-making skills. It recognises that individuals can freely make informed choices only when they are able to:

- obtain information for themselves
- make some assessment of its validity
- cope with uncertainty where knowledge is still developing
- decide that the advice is applicable to them.

The problem with this model is that individuals may be able to evaluate advice and make a rational decision to act. Yet there may still be constraints on taking action. They may not value themselves enough. They may not have the skills necessary to act, such as assertiveness skills. Or they may lack access to the resources and conditions necessary for action.

iii The self-empowerment model

This model aims to enhance self-esteem and encourage personal growth, so that individuals are able to value themselves and others. The underlying assumption is that individuals must feel that they are worth looking after, and that they must have the confidence to act. Health educators working with this approach encourage people to see themselves as a potential force for change, rather than as figures controlled by unresponsive external agents. Health skills are seen as closely related to life and social skills.

Those making use of this approach must be aware that:

- a self-empowered individual is free to choose a different set of priorities from those held by health professionals and educators
- even self-empowered groups may face difficulty in changing organisations and social structures
- overcoming material deprivation and social disadvantage requires more than life and social skills.

iv The action-for-change model

Social change takes place both from the top and from the bottom. Public health measures, better housing, improved food supply and greater purchasing power are significant factors in improving the health status of populations. In some eyes, legislation and policy changes are a more powerful means of improving health than voluntary behaviour. It is changes in the environment which make real choice possible for individuals. The project named this approach: Action-for-change 1. Health educators working with this strategy seek to influence policy makers to introduce changes conducive to health.

The action-for-change approach may also include working with groups in the community, the workplace and the educational institution, supporting them in persuading government, local authorities and other agencies to improve health by meeting the needs of the group concerned. Consumer action may pressure producers to make changes or risk losing profits. The project named this strategy: Action-for-change 2.

There are many benefits to the action-for-change model. However, it is important to remember that:

- top–down change that is unwelcome and unenforceable is likely to fail
- a change that is not monitored may have limited effectiveness, even if popularly supported
- change that is not adequately focused or resourced is unlikely to lead to the desired outcomes.

Figure 2 illustrates how each of these health education models can be located on two different dimensions : one dimension reflects the shift in emphasis between 'expert-led' and 'client-centred' approaches, the other shows changes in emphasis between 'individuals' and 'social structures'.

Fig. 2. Map of approaches to health education

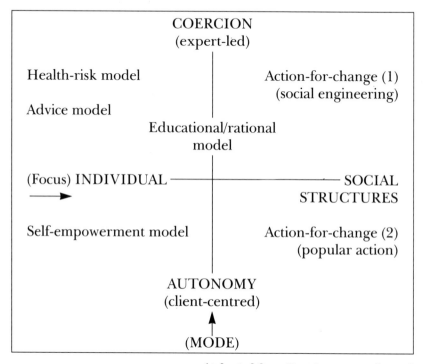

(Adapted from Beattie, 1980 and 1986)

Guide to good practice

Limiting health education interventions to any one approach will result in limited effectiveness. The first step is to identify the outcome intended from any particular health education action. The range of health education approaches must then be appraised, to identify those which will produce outcomes closest to the ones intended.

Summary

This chapter restates the commitment of the World Health Organisation to a positive model of health, rather than one which rests solely on the absence of disease. It identifies both the individual and the social parameters of health. It explains the reasons why Britain needs to undertake education directed at the achievement of positive health. It sets out the project's framework of four models of health education. It explains the view of the project that this four-fold classification mirrors the shift in FE curriculum thinking away from teacher-centred approaches and towards student-centred learning. It identifies the potential strengths and drawbacks of each of the four models: the health-risk advice model; the educational/rational model; the self-empowerment model; and the action-for-change model.

Health promotion in further education: a management perspective

3

The agenda for the 1990s

Considerable changes are facing further education during the
1990s. A wide-ranging review of the rationale of post-16
provision is occurring. This is having to take into account shifts
in the demographic pattern of the 16+ student body and
changes in the economic infrastructure. Furthermore, since
1 April 1993, it is set in the context of FE colleges as
independent corporations responsible for their own financial
affairs. To survive and flourish, colleges will need to match the
efficiency of their private sector competitors in the provision of
training and development, while at the same time maximising
their effectiveness as centres of learning for both young people
and for adults.

Effectiveness and efficiency: the health contribution

In the context of a college, promoting the health and well-being
of all members means promoting effective learning. *Managing
Colleges Efficiently* (DES/LAA, 1987) specified that the efficiency
of a college was to be regularly reviewed, and was to be
measured against its development plan. The development plan
was required to take into account employment and community
needs (in terms of range and diversity), as well as quality and
equity. *Managing Colleges Efficiently* stressed that, within these
considerations, achieving the purposes of the educational
process should not be marginalised. The full implications of
corporate status are yet to be seen. However, it is clear that
college managers will be increasingly accountable to governors

for retention and completion rates. These will be seen as vital measures of the outcomes of the educational process. *Education and Training for the 21st Century* specifies that incorporated colleges will be expected to provide information about the quality assurance systems they have in place (DES, 1991, vol. 2). While the detail is not yet available, systems for measuring satisfaction, retention and completion rates will inevitably figure.

An important contribution to achieving sound rates of retention and completion is careful focus on the needs of individual learners. Opportunities to negotiate learning objectives and to recognise and identify achievement, alongside the valuing of student-centred and participatory learning strategies, are key elements in the successful completion of a learning programme. These are also activities which enhance and develop the motivation and personal effectiveness of students. In this respect, therefore, they contribute to individual health and well-being. Through them, a sense of self-worth is reflected and encouraged by the staff and the institution. Increased interpersonal skills make successful learning outcomes more likely. Successful learning experience, in turn, makes it more likely that the college will meet its targets for retention and completion.

In the late 1980s, consultations on the nature of a post-16 core curriculum led many LEAs to consider the concept of a common learner entitlement (Further Education Unit, 1989). With college incorporation, it is not clear how these policies will evolve. However, concern for health and well-being should clearly continue to be an important component in a core curriculum entitlement for the following reasons:

- It emphasises crucial aspects of learners' past and present learning experiences (continuity and progression)
- It promotes personal and social development, and prepares learners for adult life (broad and balanced curriculum)
- It contributes to processes that recognise the different needs and learners (equal opportunities).

Equal opportunities

The social groups that are under-represented in continuing education are the same that suffer disproportionately from the major causes of illness and death in this country. The total proportion of young people going into further and higher education has traditionally always been low in the UK, compared with the rest of Europe (Handy, 1989). Further education enrolment is now being affected, in addition, by the overall downturn in the birthrate which has occurred since the mid-1960s. Yet, within these trends there is a significant social class variation, and the take-up of further and higher education places has typically been drawn disproportionately from professional groups. Colleges have already recognised the need to attract a higher proportion of the 16–19 group, as well as to bring in much greater numbers of adult learners. There is now a strong case to add social class to gender and race when seeking to increase access to, and maximise the outcomes of, learning. Increasing access to continuing education for these groups should be seen as a way, correspondingly, to increase their access to the benefits of health.

FE quality and responsiveness: the health dimension

Individual needs

The demands on colleges in the 1990s are likely to emphasise the delivery of more learning programmes that are flexible and customised to fit in with the needs of the individual young person or adult, or the organisations for whom they work. Colleges will have to consider the need to be 'open all hours', and to offer individualised programmes which have an emphasis on learning rather than teaching. Clients will expect choice, and are likely to demand improved conditions for learning. The college environment, as well as the curriculum, will be under scrutiny. Colleges will need to offer good quality working conditions for staff and students in attractive, cared-for surroundings. This will influence support services, and the provision of facilities to meet the need for child care, adequate toilet arrangements and 'fast food' services. As colleges become centres for the pursuit of individual programmes at varying times of the day and the week, potential learners are likely to be attracted to those which provide the most satisfactory environment and the best opportunities for personal health and well-being.

Under the terms of the 1988 Education Reform Act, and within the framework of the LEA strategic plan, the financial and legal powers of colleges were extended. The focus on managing colleges 'in the interests of educational effectiveness and value for money' (DES, 1987) was sharpened. The change brought new responsibilities, but also new freedoms. Colleges gained the power to 'vire' resources. Within existing constraints, they could direct their budgets as much as possible towards their own perceived priorities, in response to community and employment needs. The opportunity therefore arose to consider improving opportunities for effective learning, through maximising concern for health throughout the organisation as a whole. Under incorporation, the move to financial independence will be completed. The government intends that these changes will enable colleges to raise participation and boost achievement (DES, 1991, vol. 2).

Colleges will be completely free to choose whether or not to amplify health concerns. Colleges which choose to promote health will face the need also to promote the rationale behind their choice. They must be in a position to present the potential benefits of their approach in achieving effective learning outcomes, and providing good value for money. These benefits may need to be explained to individuals. Or they may need to be justified to the employer organisations which are sponsoring the individuals.

The human resource development function will be highlighted by those colleges that wish to grow and develop. It is increasingly recognised by the private sector, and by large public sector employers such as the Health Service, that, to ensure a healthy and growing organisation, it is essential to secure the health and well-being of all individual members. *Education and Training for the 21st Century* makes it plain that the individual is at the heart of the policy: 'Young people must be given every opportunity to progress and fulfil their potential.' They must have the 'best possible start for working in the next century' (DES, 1991, vol. 2). It is the contention of *The Health-*

promoting College that health education is essential to the achievement of these objectives, but colleges may have to fight against the continuing influence of out-dated management cultures which do not recognise this, and which are tempted to make a low priority of human resource development issues.

Colleges will face major decisions in this area. They will lose access to the free network of services provided by the local education authorities. These have supported human resource development and occupational health functions for staff. For example, colleges may now need to provide redundancy counselling. Similarly, in order to ensure quality provision in student health care, they will need to step up their school liaison and student support services. The latter have an important role to play as a focus for health promotion in colleges, particularly in relation to counselling dealing with psychological problems and use of drugs, and providing advice for students on HIV and AIDS.

The employer organisations

There is a potentially fruitful context for acceptance of the promotion of health concerns among employer organisations. A growing number of organisations recognise the value of incorporating the promotion of health and the prevention of illness into their responsibilities as employers. Organisations are concerned with the impact on their workforce of health issues such as alcohol, smoking, stress management and fitness. There is interest in the gain which can be made from the encouragement of personal effectiveness and collaboration across organisational divisions, and in adopting management styles and communication networks which develop this. Peters and Waterman (1982) call this 'productivity through people'.

Key features of the health-promoting college: the views of senior college managers

In the argument presented above, both the college and the client stand to benefit from the planning and promoting of health, whether in its narrower or its fuller 'whole person' concept.

However, to be effective, health education must be multifaceted and it must pervade the whole organisation. In other words, the college must in itself be a totally 'health-promoting' institution.

So what is a health-promoting college? What are the features senior college managers consider it should possess? In order to explore the concept of the health-promoting college more fully, and in order to view it from a management perspective, a workshop was held during the project's three-day residential conference. At this event, the senior managers identified a number of features. These were subsequently endorsed at later staff development events. The features initially developed within the project were then organised into the framework presented in Figure 3. In this diagram, significant aspects of the health-promoting college are set out within a framework of four key institutional determinants:

- the institution
- the environment
- the curriculum
- the staff–student relationship.

Fig. 3. Key features of the health-promoting college

Guide to good practice

The curriculum

- Health education across courses and integrated into the curriculum
- Effective tutorial systems, including development of personal effectiveness and health skills
- Negotiated objectives, student-centred learning experiences and recognition of achievement
- Balanced workloads
- Equal opportunities reflected across the curriculum
- Recreational and exercise options
- Staff development programmes to enable delivery of above

The institution

- Clear and consistent processes for policy and decision making that are open and represent all sections of the college
- Support available to encourage and enable staff to

contribute to innovation

- Organisational procedures and management strategies geared to recognise and reduce stress
- Cultural values that reflect concern for the well-being of college members

The environment

- Attractive, cared-for surroundings
- Good quality work conditions
- Health and safety requirements positively observed (heating, lighting, ventilation, toilet/washing facilities and repair of structure)
- Facilities: quiet room, recreation and exercise, religious observance, specific needs arising from interpretations of equal opportunities policies; group and individual study
- A smoke-free environment
- Wide-ranging catering provision including

availability of 'healthy' choices

- Crèche and play-scheme facilities that observe the extended college year
- Removal of graffiti that contravene equal opportunities policies

Staff–student relationship

- Counselling service
- Staff/student contact beyond teaching-related commitments
- Health guidance accessible to all
- Student involvement in policy making
- Effective internal communications for and with students as well as staff
- Good support services in sufficient quantities to enable student-centred and problem solving learning to take place
- Happy atmosphere: respect and responsibility
- Commitment to active learning strategies

Summary

This chapter sets out the arguments for college managers in
favour of viewing health education as a potentially significant
contributor to college efficiency and effectiveness. It suggests
that, with incorporation, the impact of improved conditions for
health and well-being on key college indicators, such as
retention and completion rates, is likely to be favourable. It
shows that health education has a contribution to make to the
issues of equal opportunities, quality and responsiveness
whether to the needs of the individual or employer clients. As a
guide to good practice, the chapter presents a framework
demonstrating the features of the health-promoting college.
Four key institutional determinants are considered: the
institution; the environment; the curriculum; the staff–student
relationship.

The health-promoting college: development issues   4

A model for developing the health-promoting college emerged
from the project's findings (Figure 4). Commitment to
achieving the goal of becoming a health-promoting college must
be placed in the college's mission statement. But it must also be
reflected in the college's plan for the allocation of resources.
Furthermore, the institution's ethos and setting, the curriculum,
and the values and skills of staff must all be developed. All
aspects must be developed jointly if the college is to achieve its
goal of becoming a health-promoting organisation.

Fig. 4. Developing the health-promoting college

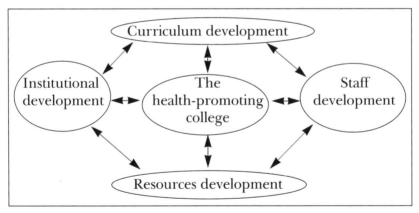

Institutional development

The built environment and services

It is possible to review a college's physical setting simply in the light of its general state of repair, or within the minimum requirements of health and safety. However, managers will not need reminding that any college which wishes to be seen as a serious contender in an expanded market for education and training needs to go well beyond minimum provision. So must a college which wishes to take the promotion of health seriously. It must consider upgrading the building.

The health-promoting college: upgrading the building

✓ a review of space utilisation related to activity needs, rather than simply to the number of bodies needing to be accommodated
✓ decor that is conducive to productive work and shows respect for the users
✓ a high standard of basic facilities and services; including as a minimum:
> toilets
> crèche
> food
> rest-rooms/sick-bay
> and communal lounges

✓ planning for a phased move beyond the minimum facilities; for example, provision for:
> exercise, including showers
> individual and group study
> extracurricular activities
> organised by staff and/or
> students
> space available for community use.

The culture of the college

The health-promoting college needs to consider its formal organisational culture.

The health-promoting college: reviewing the culture

✓ What is the college culture?

✓ Is it widely shared?
✓ Are there sub-cultures?
   If there are sub-cultures, are they actually or potentially
   supportive to the concept of the health-promoting
   college? Or are they in opposition?
✓ Do the shared values serve a real purpose?
   Are they keeping pace with the changes in further
   education?

Management style

As college managers are well aware, the style of management
sets the tone for the pattern of interpersonal relationships and
the general ethos of the college. An organisation that aims to
promote health needs to pay continuous attention to this fact.
Managing change puts these concerns into sharp focus. Anxiety
about job losses, changes in approach or structural changes can
cause breakdown of relationships and trust. These in turn
undermine efforts to meet changing demands from outside.
Open, honest and dependable communication may not only
help to prevent anxiety from becoming destructive, but also
provides a wider forum for problem solving and innovation.
Support staff and the student body should be consulted on the
same basis as teaching staff. This recognises their needs and
their contribution. It also acknowledges the expanded role of
support services in newly developing forms of learning delivery.

The health-promoting college: aspects of management style

✓ open information networks
✓ participation in decision making
✓ recognition of contribution and achievement
✓ well-balanced and inclusive patterns of professional,
   personal and industrial relations
✓ priority given to human resource development and
   occupational health issues.

Curriculum development

An integrated approach to health promotion and health education

The overall goal is to integrate health education into the curriculum of the whole range of programmes. As FE staff will be aware, this is very different from bolting it on. Planning and development over defined periods of time is needed. A system for monitoring and evaluating the process of development and its outcomes must be in place. To achieve any real progress active involvement in integrated health education at course team level is essential.

Health education that is restricted to health-risk advice is unlikely to be effective. Instead, it needs to combine the exploration of health themes and health topics with the development of health skills. Individuals must be able to assess health advice, and relate it to their own lives. They must develop the capacity to value health, and to secure their own health and that of others.

To achieve this, learning opportunities are needed which develop personal and social skills. Learners should become self-directed and take responsibility for themselves. Individuals must be given the chance to engage in problem solving and student-centred learning. These encourage decision making and action planning. Self-confidence and interpersonal skills develop, and these benefit the overall learning process. A focus on health skills makes a substantial contribution to a core curriculum which wishes to emphasise that the quality of the experience of learning is a significant aspect of the desired outcome.

Staff development

Acceptance of health education

All staff development is dependent on curriculum-led activities. To develop commitment to the value of health education and to gain understanding of the approaches that enhance its effectiveness, staff need training and support.

The project's finding was that responsiveness to its curriculum initiatives was highest among staff working on programmes including explicit concern for personal and social effectiveness, negotiation of learning and use of integrated assignments. Such staff were associated with initiatives such as TVEI, CPVE, YTS training, some BTEC programmes and other courses involving a tutorial element. Take-up of training and co-tutoring, and interest in planning future action, were greatest with this group of staff.

Developing learning styles, core skills and cross-curricular themes

Staff will need to consider how their students might have access to a range of learning styles and core skills, including personal and social effectiveness, as well as access to cross-curricular health education. Colleges need to consider what staff development in core skills is needed. They need to decide whether a specialist team should be developed to support work on health topics and skills.

Networking

Specialist teams can benefit from liaising with those doing similar work in other colleges. LEAs may be able to attract colleges to buy into initial training through a cross-authority offer.

The project finding was that a one-day conference run across the Birmingham colleges provided a valuable exchange of experience and ideas. It enabled college-based groups to end the day with an outline policy statement and action plan.

Staff development for support staff

The health-promoting college must consider the role of staff development for support staff. Support staff are vital to any organisation. They are especially so in the reorganisation of structures and programmes which colleges will experience in the mid-1990s.

The project findings were that there was great demand for stress management courses and many support staff expressed the feeling that their needs were treated as secondary to those of teaching staff.

Resources development

To become a health-promoting college demands a range of resources, and it is expensive. On the other hand, it can be highly cost-effective to equip a college to compete in a changing market for education and training, and to enable it to deliver what it promises to a high standard. The health-promoting college has to come into effect over time. An overall implementation strategy will be needed relating budget allocation to priorities and schedules.

The health-promoting college: a strategy

Making a start: a college conference

The value of taking an open and broad-based approach to initiating policy should be considered. Discussion of a health promotion policy at an opening conference which represents all college members, from governors through all sections of staff to the various client groups, puts the concept of the health-promoting college firmly on to the agenda. The college then begins the process of developing a realistic action-plan.

Support from other agencies: developing an action strategy

Other agencies can help the college both in developing an action strategy and in specific task areas. The health promotion/education units of District Health Authorities may be able to act as consultants and contribute to the development of training programmes, as well as advise on strategy and schedules for change. They may also act as a channel to draw on the professional experience of other DHA personnel such as dietitians, as well as providing a link to national resources such as the Health Education Authority and the projects it commissions and disseminates. Other local agencies should also be canvassed.

A planning model

A model for planning the health-promoting college is presented in Figure 5. It combines a focus on structures with the process of influencing learning programmes.

On a number of distinct issues (see Chapter 5), the college may benefit from a specific health promotion policy; for example, policies on smoking, alcohol, HIV and AIDS. This demonstrates the college's commitment to contribute to the health of its members. There may also be implications for its practice in relation to personnel matters and equal opportunities.

Fig. 5. Introducing health promotion to the college structure and programmes

Summary

This chapter outlines a four-fold model for developing the health-promoting college. The aspects of this are: institutional development, which covers the built environment of the college, its culture and its management style; curriculum development; staff development, including the development of support staff; and resources development. It suggests that an effective strategy for getting started is to open discussion of a health promotion policy at a college conference.

Major aspects of health: practical strategies for a college 5

Introduction

Focus on specific threats to health

Chapter 2 highlighted the importance of placing health in the broad context of well-being, and personal effectiveness is emphasised. It also, however, identified a number of areas which pose particular threats to health. These provide the focus of this chapter. The experience of the project is used to illustrate a range of practical strategies which can be used to tackle such topics in a college setting. In addition, the constraints which may operate are also illustrated.

This chapter makes it clear that achieving a healthy college has implications for all the developmental aspects of a college (see Chapter 4). Of particular importance are those related to curriculum, staff and the institutional ethos. Furthermore, approaches to health education within the healthy college must select from and combine the full range of health education models. In other words, to achieve an environment which is health promoting rather than illness inducing, a setting must be created in which learning opportunities, experience and working conditions all act *in harmony*.

The structure of the chapter

To introduce this chapter, the models of health education illustrated earlier are set out again (see Figure 6). Types of action which characterise each approach, and which could be applied in a college setting, are summarised within each of the classifications. In addition, the need for integration and coherence is emphasised. A discussion of seven specific health topics then follows. This illustrates a variety of organisational strategies and health education approaches which could be used in a college. The topics are: diet and healthy food choices; smoking; HIV/AIDS and sexual health; stress; exercise and health-related fitness; alcohol and its use; and drug and solvent abuse. For two of the topics (smoking and stress), diagrams are included (Figures 8 and 9). These illustrate how the four health education models (health-risk advice; educational/rational; self-empowerment; action-for-change) can be integrated with the four aspects of institutional development (environment; curriculum; staff–student relationships; institution).

Fig. 6. Models of health education

Model	Aim	Action in colleges
Health-risk advice	To inform, advise and modify behaviour (coerce or persuade).	Leaflets in library. Talks, videos, visitors, displays. Fitness tests.
Educational/rational	To provide access to information and to promote understanding. To explore values and attitudes. To foster rational choice and decision making.	Problem-solving work in the curriculum.
Self-empowerment	To foster self-esteem and development of interpersonal and life skills. To encourage and support self-direction and identify the scope for choice.	Groupwork to develop life and health skills. Personal effectiveness and health skills through group tutorials and collaborative, student-centred learning across the curriculum.
Action-for-change *Top–down*	To change organisations and communities to facilitate healthier choices. To reduce inequalities and promote equality of opportunity.	Improve setting; allocate resources to further student-centred learning.
Bottom–up	To encourage group problem solving. To foster critical social analysis.	Student and staff participation in decision making; secure ownership of policy across college; work with real-life situations.

Current curriculum changes and integrated health education

The curriculum in further education is undergoing substantial change at present. None the less, it offers opportunities to integrate health education topics into the full range of courses, both for the current range of pre-vocational and vocational education (CPVE, BTECs, and so on), and for the General National Vocational Qualifications (GNVQs) which are planned to replace them. There is no need to bolt on additional layers to already dense syllabuses. Health topics, such as those discussed in this chapter, can contribute directly to course objectives and learning outcomes in GCSE, GCE A level and GNVQ programmes. They can also contribute to the curriculum entitlement offered to students following work-related education and training, towards assessment for the emerging framework of NVQs (National Vocational Qualifications), across all occupational areas.

Health education is identified as a cross-curricular theme in the National Curriculum Council's non-statutory publication *Curriculum Guidance 5: Health Education* (NCC, 1990). This guidance outlines nine components of a health education curriculum for 5- to 16-year-olds. It also provides appropriate areas of study in each of the components, outlining the knowledge, skills and attitudes to be acquired by young people for each key stage. Many areas identified for key stage 4 have continuing relevance for the post-16 age group, and further education is able to take this into account in planning health education programmes.

To seek the input of external advice and help is useful. Health matters can be complex, and there is a range of specialist bodies able to assist college staff by making a contribution to the topics discussed in this chapter.

Health topics in the curriculum

Health topics can contribute directly to the development of core skills and course objectives in all areas. For example:

Science
investigating analysis to supply nutritional labelling; investigating the constituents of pesticides, controls on usage and safety testing procedures and standards; investigating the effects of alcohol on the individual

Technology
considering the impact of process innovation

Mathematics
exploring statistics, worldwide incidence and distribution

Social studies
tastes and expectations: factors which influence them;
the impact of industry on policy making in health areas

Communication
body image;
media study – exploring the effect of advertising on
eating habits;
health promotion strategies;
alcohol and relationships

Business
exploring government directives, statutory and
voluntary codes of practice (for example, the voluntary
agreement on alcohol advertising);
stress management

Engineering
investigating design and maintenance of equipment

Health and social care
health promotion;
design of health promotion activities

Leisure and tourism
promoting fitness;
investigating customer tastes and needs;
access to alcohol in leisure time (for example, effects of
increased licensing hours)

Work experience
Health and safety regulations: analysis of
implementation;
smoking and alcohol policies;
fitness and diet issues

A coherent framework for active learning

A coherent curriculum framework, which should be the aim of
every college for the 16–19 age group, will offer scope for
health education and health promotion, both within specific
qualification routes and throughout activities set up to develop
the core skills of communication, numeracy, information
technology, and problem-solving and personal skills. The

National Record of Achievement (NRA) will be issued to all GNVQ students, and its use will be encouraged with all other students. Higher education is also recognising its potential value in relation to degree programmes (Deere, 1992).

Within the NRA there is scope to demonstrate the extent to which students are able to be pro-active in their role as learners. Opportunities are given for students to record participation in activities and events of the type illustrated in this chapter.

It is important to note that the process of reflecting on and recording learning is a powerful process for enhancing self-esteem. This in itself contributes to student confidence and sense of well-being. Figure 7 demonstrates how the four health education models can be related to an increasingly active role for students in their own learning.

Fig. 7. Health education in the curriculum

Models	Methods/action	Student role
Health-risk advice	Events, displays, leaflets. Talks. Video/film. Workpacks.	Passive recipient: low level of participation.
Educational/ rational	Problem solving: individually and in groups. Workpacks. Checklists, brainstorms, buzz-groups, trigger-films.	Active but reactively so. Some scope for input and negotiation.
Self-empowerment	Work with groups: interpersonal skills, constructive feedback; experiential: self-disclosure and reflective. Role play/ simulation/real-life situations.	Pro-actively active. Work collaboratively and share with others. Full engagement.
Action-for-change	Action-based and related to real-life situations. Includes changing the college. Groupwork strategies.	Pro-active and collaborative. Negotiate issues, content and process. View college as a variable not a given.

(Adapted from: Ryder and Campbell, 1988)

Lecturer/tutor role	Institution role	Evaluation /assessment of health education action
Organise; liaise. Introduce visitor. Be the expert, in control of knowledge.	Funds, good contacts, display boards, leaflet racks. Tolerate/welcome events and visitors.	Test knowledge of individual. Summative and norm referenced. Pass or fail. Use tests, exams, written work.
Organise/liaise behind scenes. Select issues and content. Arbitrator; guide to 'beacon'. Persuader. Director.	Provide resources to enable use of problem solving: time to develop; team options; materials; appropriate work-rooms and equipment.	Can look at process as well as outcomes. Formative as well as summative. Related to individual: criterion referenced. Skills and attitudes change.
Facilitator. Less directive but provides 'safe' frameworks. Enables.	Provide resources and facilitate organisationally: timetabling, co-tutoring; variety of rooms. Will not find one lecturer and whole class in one room for each session.	Formative and criterion referenced. Looks for negotiated competencies in process and outcomes. Some self-assessment. Over time, increases in self-esteem, interpersonal skills and overall health status.
Negotiate boundaries. Energise; facilitate.	Agenda-setting: top–down policy or encourage participation and collective ownership of policy.	Formative and criterion referenced. Group-based with group determining criteria. Summative over effects of action.

1. Diet and healthy food choices

The reasons for action

Food choices can create stress and conflict in families and households. Stress in its own right can lead to poor eating choices. Some individuals may feel that they are more controlled by, than in control of, their food consumption. The opportunity to develop personal effectiveness and health skills contributes to people's ability to manage these issues. In addition, dietary patterns are now implicated in a number of diseases. Current guidelines recommend that as a nation we should reduce our intake of fats, sugars and salt, and increase our intake of fibre-rich, starchy food (DH, 1991). The evidence suggests that many people, especially women, are aware of these recommendations, as well as being concerned with other issues such as food additives. However, the project finding was that individuals perceive difficulties in putting advice into practice because of a number of factors. These include: cost; availability of appropriate foods; expectations of those being catered for; and making healthy food choices when time and labour are limited.

The college institution and environment: food-related issues

Food choices in the canteen

If the canteen facilities are entirely a college responsibility, the college should consider including affordable and culturally acceptable healthy food choices that can be readily identified as such. If using contracted providers, the college or the LEA should consider including healthy eating, within a multi-cultural frame, in its criteria for tenders at the next review of contracts. In the meantime, it may be possible to negotiate moves towards such provision.

The project discovered that the caterers for the Birmingham city colleges wished to develop their existing food health policy. Areas identified for action included training for canteen managers; promotion of the canteen's range of healthy choices; and the development of an evaluation strategy. Sources of support are available to colleges in this area. When acting on them, colleges will need to take account of the training needs of staff and the available budget:

- the DHA can be approached to provide consultancy support and may be able to provide a database on food supplies and catering contractors that promote healthy eating
- a forward-thinking catering enterprise might consider commissioning a suitable agency to promote its provisions for healthy food choices
- colleges may be able to draw on their developing marketing expertise, or students may wish to design and launch a promotional campaign in a real-life setting.

Guide to good practice

Questions to ask:

- Does the college canteen provide scope for making healthy food choices?
- If it does, are the student views of the choice known?
- Is the take-up of healthy choices high or low?
- Can the customers afford the food of their choice?
- Does the canteen promote healthy eating?
- Does the menu identify and promote healthy choices?
- Do the healthy choices reflect a multi-cultural approach?

There is scope for action if the answer to any of the above questions is negative, or if the take-up of healthy choices is low, relative to less healthy choices.

Canteen accommodation

A fog of tobacco smoke, faded and grubby decor and conventional canteen furniture which is in poor repair do not encourage considerate use of the accommodation. Neither do they reflect a college's goals to meet student needs positively. Colleges should consider upgrading canteen facilities to a similar standard to those provided by customer-oriented firms in the private sector. The provision of no-smoking areas is important.

The college curriculum: food topics

Curriculum areas

A number of curriculum areas offer opportunities for incorporation of health education in relation to diet. The production, distribution and consumption of food on local, national and international scales provide a rich field for exploring diet and nutrition. Catering, health studies and retail courses are obvious examples. It cannot be assumed that such courses already introduce the topic of diet and healthy food choices effectively. Constraints include inadequate understanding of current nutritional guidelines, and the perception that qualification-awarding bodies do not include adequate scope for exploring healthy eating issues.

There are important issues relating to food choices which need to be raised. The reasons why many individuals feel that they should diet, and the strategies they use for losing weight, are an example. There are related issues arising from this to do with the labelling and presentation of food to the consumer.

Awards are currently available in basic food handling. The Environmental Health Office offers a certificate in Basic Food Hygiene. The Hotel and Catering Training Company (HCTC) offers an award in Hygiene for the Food Handler, approved by the Royal Institute of Health and Hygiene.

Current NVQ National Standards refer to aspects of safety in food handling, where appropriate, in the Standards that relate to the preparation, cooking and serving of food. Relevant units guarantee, through the Range Indicators, that candidates know the requirements of all relevant legislation. Units which relate to menu planning also raise issues concerned with nutrition.

Following publication of the White Paper *The Health of the Nation: a Strategy for Health in England* (DH, 1992), it is likely that the multisectoral taskforce will look at aspects of nutrition and healthy eating, within training standards for the hotel and catering industry.

The training restaurant

Courses involving training restaurants could consider a Health Education Authority Heartbeat Award. Participants must demonstrate that those running the restaurant consistently meet specified standards of hygiene, offer healthy food choices as standard practice, and ensure that one-third of the seating area is set aside for non-smokers.

The project explored this idea with catering staff in the pilot college, and established that, while many courses did include food hygiene, students may simply obtain a specific qualification for food handler, such as the Basic Food Hygiene certificate. However, the college training restaurant did already implement non-smoking seating, which has become standard information asked for when booking a table.

Legislation has now been instituted, the Food Safety Act 1990, which incorporates hygiene standards and establishes training requirements for all food handlers (MAFF, 1989).

Colleges should recognise that the various food industry sectors – agriculture, manufacturing, retail and catering – are facing some challenge from consumers regarding the composition of food, in terms of nutritional advice and additives.

2. Smoking

The reasons for action

Smoking-related diseases contribute to death and disability on a large scale. While the prevalence of adult cigarette smoking in Great Britain has declined, research indicates that 25 per cent of boys and girls aged 15–16 are regular smokers (OPCS, 1991). Research has also shown that smoking prevalence in 16-year-olds at further education colleges varies according to the vocational subject being studied. For example, 50 per cent of hairdressers and 44 per cent of pre-nursing students have been found to be regular smokers (Charlton, 1983).

Recent research has confirmed that non-smokers exposed to long-term passive smoking are also at risk. Leading cancer scientists estimate the risk of lung cancer from passive smoking to be at least some 50 to 100 times the risk from exposure to asbestos in buildings (ASH,1988).

The optimum college strategy therefore seems likely to be the adoption of a smoking policy at institutional level, supported by curriculum development.

The college institution and environment: smoking

A smoking policy

Colleges need to consider whether they can afford to be *without* a smoking policy. It is essential that students and staff are able to spend their time in college in a smoke-free environment. Colleges will benefit from a number of factors:

- reduced absenteeism
- increased productivity
- a cleaner environment and reduced cleaning and decoration costs
- improved staff morale
- reduced fire risk
- reduced ventilation and air-conditioning costs.

The Health, Safety and Welfare at Work Act 1974 requires an employer to provide and maintain '. . . a working environment for his employees that is, so far as is reasonably practicable, safe, without risks to health, and adequate as regards facilities and arrangements for their welfare at work' (section 2(2)(*e*)).

It is probable that a non-smoking employee could take action against an employer who fails to provide a smoke-free environment and thereby fails to protect the health of the workforce. The onus is now on employers to act in advance of legal changes.

Guide to good practice

The following issues are recommended for consideration when establishing the policy:

1　Purpose and approach
- Establish no smoking as the norm
- Anti-smoking not anti-smoker
- Response to a health and safety issue.

2   *Working party*
- Representatives of all sections of college and of smoking experience
- Could be *ad hoc* or sub-group of the health and safety committee.

3   *Information campaign and survey*
- Early announcement of rationale for policy
- Assess views and experience of college members.

4   *Draft policy*
- State purpose and identify the areas where smoking may be allowed
- Make policy statement short and clear
- Put guidelines for implementation in a separate document.

5   *Consultation and review*
- Encourage ownership of the policy
- Seek helpful suggestions and note constraints
- Finalise policy statement and guidelines for implementation
- Ensure that relevant contracted services are included.

6   *Ratify*
- Take to the appropriate college bodies as college policy.

7   *Resources*
- Cost out and allocate a budget to establish and maintain the policy.

8   *Implementation*
- Choose an opportune time to implement the policy
- Provide clear information on the areas where people may smoke
- Ensure these are clearly marked
- Arrange for support for those giving up smoking.

9   *Monitoring*
- It is crucial that the policy is monitored and reviewed at a senior level.

Issues in implementation of a no-smoking policy

The main pilot college undertook action to implement its smoking policy across the college from the start of the 1988/89 academic year. While the project observed efforts to respect the policy initially, non-compliance set in within weeks in a number of areas. Analysis of the problems and subsequent action by project staff have highlighted the need to be thorough in all the steps outlined above. In particular, the following areas were found to be important:

Survey of college members
A high response rate can be expected from staff, and the most likely outcome is a clear majority in favour of a smoke-free working environment. Surveying the student body is more difficult. If the institution does not already have a system that offers a good response rate, it may benefit by developing an effective means of obtaining feedback from students on college policy matters. It is important that students as well as staff own the policy.

No-smoking signs
In canteens that provide for both smokers and non-smokers, boundaries need to be completely clear. The project recommends the use of screens or planters to identify the areas, as well as signs. Paper table-top signs were found to be short-lived and ineffective.

Compliance and enforcement
Sooner or later an organisation the size of a college will face problems of enforcement. While flexibility and tolerance are needed, especially at the outset, failure to deal firmly and consistently with continued breaches will undermine the policy and raise questions about fairness. The project finding was that staff compliance has generally been good. However, support staff who smoke may feel badly affected in comparison with other staff because they are less able to build smoking breaks into their work. Breaches of the policy by senior staff tend to cause concern among both non-smokers and smokers, and the sharing of a relatively small communal area by smokers and non-smokers causes problems for many non-smokers, especially at peak-use time.

Achieving compliance among students is more difficult. Weak areas are corridors, concourses and canteens or lounges. The project did not find a solution to this problem, but it must involve influencing the culture of the college to respect the right of non-smokers. The project's experience is that senior managers have a key role in this respect. This is likely to involve both smokers and non-smokers requesting that the policy be observed. Feeling able and willing to do this may require the development of assertiveness and other interpersonal skills within the college.

Monitoring

Monitoring of the policy is crucial. This can be greatly assisted by those who see and deal with the concrete evidence, such as the building supervisors and cleaners.

Stop-smoking support

The project concluded that there was a large response by staff to a stop-smoking course when the smoking policy was introduced. Take-up by students may be greater where they are involved in the establishment of the policy, and explore some of the issues within their courses. Take-up may vary both by college and by year, and may be related to how far awareness of the policy reaches. Where there is a need for help in giving up, it is important that the college responds. Advice on the strengths and limitations of various stop-smoking programmes may be obtained from the college's local health promotion unit.

Ventilation

Air purification and ventilation equipment is not a feasible solution, especially in a communal area. Costs of adequate air change are high, air-conditioning systems may spread smoke around the building, and airborne carcinogens and carbon monoxide tend to remain.

The college curriculum: smoking

The background

The evidence shows that young children are aware that smoking is a health risk, and have a reasonable knowledge of which diseases are smoking related. The problem is clearly not lack of awareness or knowledge. The majority of established adult smokers would prefer to stop but find the physiological and psychological dependence hard to break. Young people starting to smoke or in the early part of their smoking careers say they want to fit in or be sociable. Some view smoking as a means of relaxing or as part of their culture.

Health education that only emphasises the health-related risks of smoking is unlikely to lead to behaviour changes. It should therefore help people to:

- examine the social and economic interests involved in smoking
- explore the reasons why people start to smoke, and why they continue
- develop the interpersonal skills needed to resist smoking, or to assert a desire for a smoke-free environment.

Guide to good practice

The above objectives can be sought in group tutorials or within course modules. Some examples include:

- ✓ courses on gender differentiation could consider the smoking issues specific to women
- ✓ smoking in the workplace could be explored through health and safety matters, industrial relations and personnel concerns, or the design and workings of ventilation systems
- ✓ No Smoking Day could be a vehicle for student-centred work in real-life situations across a range of learning programmes.

Finally, to sum up, the topic of smoking is used in Figure 8 to illustrate the way that an aspect of health education can be thoroughly integrated with institutional development, within the health-promoting college.

Fig. 8. Smoking

Model	Environment	Curriculum	Staff–student relationships	Institution
Health-risk advice	Provide advice on passive smoking.	Visitor sessions on risks of smoking.	Exhibition for staff and students on National No Smoking Day.	Give clear notice that in the health interests of its students the college has restricted smoking to designated areas.
Educational/rational	Survey college members to assess their desire for a smoke-free environment.	Examine the reasons why people start and continue to smoke. Examine the social and economic interests in smoking.	Encourage smoking cessation groups for staff and students.	Engage in promotional work that actively involves the students.
Self-empowerment	Enable college members to actively uphold the no-smoking policy.	Develop the inter-personal skills to resist smoking.	Encourage people wishing to stop smoking to meet and determine their own needs and patterns of support.	Provide facilities for self-help groups.
Action-for-change	Clearly inform people of the no-smoking policy.	Carry out problem-solving assignments relevant to real-life situations, e.g. assess smoking patterns in the workplace.	Allow for student and staff participation in creating and implementing the no-smoking policy.	Show that the college recognises its responsibility to protect the health of its staff and students.

3.   HIV/AIDS and sexual health

The reasons for action

It is increasingly recognised that acquired immunodeficiency syndrome (AIDS) has the potential to become one of the greatest threats to public health this century has known. By the end of December 1992 19 065 reports of HIV antibody positive people had been received and 6929 people with AIDS (including 4291 deaths) had been reported in the UK (PHLS, 1992). This is considered to under-represent the actual prevalence of the human immunodeficiency virus (HIV), which may affect between 30 000 and 50 000 people. HIV infection is not confined to any one society, culture, gender, race, sexual orientation or age group. The number of reported cases of HIV is doubling every month.

As yet there is no vaccine against AIDS, and no cure that can eradicate the underlying immune deficiency. As well as the costs of treatment and care for a person with AIDS, social costs arise from the loss of a family member and personal networks, and through productive life lost.

What are HIV and AIDS?

AIDS is caused by a virus called HIV. This can damage the body's defence system so that it cannot fight certain infections.

It is important to recognise that it is certain behaviours which are risky, rather than certain groups of people. HIV is transmitted in three main ways:

- through unprotected sexual intercourse (anal or vaginal) with a person who is infected with HIV
- by injecting drug users sharing equipment, including syringes and needles
- from an infected mother to her unborn child.

The risk of infection from a blood transfusion in Britain is negligible. Since 1985 donated blood has been screened for antibodies to HIV. Similarly, blood plasma products such as Factor Eight, which is used by haemophiliacs, are made safe by special treatment.

The personal and social impact of HIV/AIDS is immense.

Colleges will need to ensure that individuals with HIV and AIDS are not disadvantaged in either employment or entitlement to learning opportunities. Colleges may also have to confront fear, prejudice, ignorance and discrimination.

Students need to be reassured that everyday contact with someone who has HIV or AIDS is perfectly safe. The virus cannot be passed on through touching, shaking hands or hugging; individuals cannot be infected by sharing objects used by an infected person; HIV cannot be passed on by sneezing, coughing or swimming; HIV is not known to be passed on through tears or sweat; individuals cannot be infected with HIV by mosquito and other insect bites.

The college institution and environment: HIV and AIDS

Safe practices

Colleges have a duty to ensure that safe practices are observed in relation to hygiene and infection control. The practice already being observed to prevent transmission of a range of diseases will also help to prevent transmission of HIV. Colleges may wish to consider the value of drawing up protocols for hygiene and infection control practice irrespective of whether they have known HIV positive students or not.

Training for cleaning and building supervisors

The project delivered short training sessions for the cleaning and building supervisors in the main pilot college, and devised a one-day programme for college crèche workers. The former identified some barriers to safe practice; many of those who participated welcomed the opportunity to discuss the key issues.

Guide to good practice

Colleges may wish to check that:

✓ building supervisors and cleaners have the knowledge, skills and working conditions necessary for safe hygiene practice

✓ crèche workers observe standard infection control measures and safe hygiene practice as a matter of routine

✓ first aiders and any medical and paramedical staff are updated on safe practice

✓ all staff understand their role in responding to any accident or manifestation of illness.

Safer sex

Encouraging the use of and access to condoms is a major public health issue. Colleges may also feel that they have a role in facilitating and enabling healthy choices, including measures to counter unintended pregnancy and the transmission of HIV and other sexually transmitted diseases. They may wish to consider installing condom vending machines, bearing in mind the possible religious or cultural objections. Some colleges around the country have already done this, either through a contract with a major supplier or through the DHA. The project is not aware of any problems arising in these colleges. It may be useful to consult with the relevant health educators in the local authority and health authority.

The project found that areas of concern raised by colleges included the possibility of media distortion; the possibility of causing offence to some sections of the community, both in the college and beyond it; and access by young people under the age of 16, for example, on link and TVE1/TVE courses.

Development of a policy on HIV and AIDS

As with sex education, colleges may benefit from developing a clear policy on HIV and AIDS.

Guide to good practice

A policy on HIV and AIDS should:

✓ commit the college to include HIV and AIDS awareness training in their staff development programmes

✓ provide health education across courses

- ✓ ensure that people with HIV infection or AIDS are not discriminated against in employment or in access to learning opportunities
- ✓ not include a requirement for HIV testing for staff or students
- ✓ consider installation of condom machines
- ✓ implement safer practices in hygiene and infection control.

A draft policy should be developed by a working group representing interests across the college – students, staff groups, college management and governors. The working group should consult with the appropriate local health services and personnel. Such a group could begin with a training programme, designed to enable participants to understand the issues involved in preventing HIV transmission. The project finding was that awareness-raising training was effective in identifying and understanding issues, and was an important component in the development of policy and practice.

Curriculum and staff development

A survey on the health and lifestyles of 16- to 19-year-olds living in England carried out in 1990 HEA (1992), found that only 44 per cent feel sufficiently informed about the risk of AIDS to young people. Only a minority (31 per cent) of young people feel that they may have to make some adjustment to their lifestyle because of the risk of AIDS.

Guide to good practice

Health education in colleges should allow people to:

- ✓ explore their knowledge, attitudes and fears about HIV and AIDS
- ✓ consider the personal implications of health education messages about HIV and AIDS
- ✓ identify and practise the skills needed to integrate these health messages into their lifestyles
- ✓ consider the implications of health education messages about HIV and AIDS for their own work practices
- ✓ identify collectively their own possible contributions to effective health education.

To achieve the above it will not be enough simply to convey information. It is crucial that the needs, attitudes and prior knowledge of the learner, whether staff or student, is given central importance. It may also be useful to seek advice and inputs from specialist organisations.

Staff should be aware that some people with HIV and AIDS have been treated badly and discriminated against. Students should be encouraged not to break up friendships, as friendship and support may be the most important things they can offer.

An illustrative example

To achieve a number of the objectives outlined above, the project set up sessions involving a play about health education followed by group workshops. Both the play, *Putting it About*, and the workshops were held during a common tutorial time in two of the colleges. The group size was 10–12. The groups were led by members of the theatre group. They were supported by college teaching staff who had completed an HIV/AIDS awareness course. This had been organised in-house, and delivered by specialist HIV/AIDS health education officers from the local health authorities.

Students explored fears and beliefs and to some extent clarified values. Follow-up evaluation found that students valued the opportunity to identify and explore issues concerned with the transmission and prevention of HIV and AIDS. They reported greater confidence in avoiding risk to themselves owing to their own behaviours.

The exercise was also a useful case study in the use of collaborative learning strategies, and in the inclusion of work on personal effectiveness in group tutorials.

Note. For more information on policy and practice issues concerned with HIV/AIDS see the Health Education Authority HIV/AIDS Sexual Health Paper *HIV/AIDS Education in Six Colleges* (HEA, 1993).

4. Stress

The reasons for action

Everyone experiences stress in one form or another. Some
stress is healthy; it enables a person to set and achieve goals and
to overcome difficulties. Too much stress, however, causes
strain, and can result in short-term ill health, or long-term
physical or mental damage.

Stresses can be internal or external. The stress caused by
running 100 metres in 12 seconds would cause most of us
intolerable strain; to a trained athlete the stress is tolerable.
Likewise, the stresses experienced in the classroom by new
teachers are usually far greater than those felt by experienced
teachers. Each of us experiences stress in the work situation,
and each of us copes with it with varying levels of success at
different times of our lives.

The college institution and environment: aspects of stress

It is estimated that at least 40 million working days are lost each
year owing to nervous and other ailments associated with or
exacerbated by stress (Jee and Reason, 1988). The project
obtained absence-through-sickness data from seven of the city
colleges for the period 1 January–30 November 1988. A total of
7873 days were lost owing to staff sickness across the colleges,
with sickness rates peaking in October–November and
January–February–March. Of these, 431 days were specifically
identified as stress-related.

GPs as well as individuals may be unlikely to cite stress as the
reason for absence if they feel that some stigma may result.
Physical conditions associated with stress, such as back pain,
migraine, and sickness and diarrhoea may be cited. Individuals
may phone in to present reasons for short-term sick-leave
because of colds and flu or general malaise, rather than
identifying themselves as unable to cope. Serious conditions
such as ulcers or coronary heart disease can be indicators of
severe stress.

Stress is not a form of weakness. The health-promoting
college recognises that stress can become difficult to manage,

and plans its activities so as to minimise stress and provide support for people who are at risk. This is particularly important, given the current climate of rapid change. Colleges may wish to consider whether there are signs of the following indicators of stress:

- high rates of illness
- high staff turnover
- student non-completion
- many requests for early retirement
- poor working relationships
- low morale
- increasing disputes and industrial relations cases.

Not all of these conditions are attributable to stress alone, but the presence of a high proportion of them should give cause for concern, and should direct attention towards identification of the underlying causes. It is an inadequate response to claim that times are hard and that nothing can be done.

Many organisations are unaware of the signs of unhealthy stress at work. A survey of staff in each of the three project colleges involved four open-ended questions concerning:

- experience and perceived causes of stress in both work and personal spheres
- perceived indicators of stress
- responses to any stress experienced.

A significant minority in the main project college reported that work-related stress was a problem for them. Smaller but still sizeable minorities responded in the two other colleges. It is likely that the more dominant presence of the project in the pilot college was a factor in the response rate. Overall, work-related factors were more frequently reported than others, and the areas most frequently cited were:

- feelings of overload and work/time pressure
- the physical environment
- management practices.

The college aiming to maximise effectiveness and efficiency will need to provide an environment that is conducive to the well-being of its members. Many of the factors working against this are amenable to control by the staff, particularly college management. Organisational matters, such as the relationship between college policies and practices, goals and outcomes, planned structures and actual operations, provide clues to the health of a college. Regular review of these should be a matter of routine practice.

Guide to good practice

Organisation review – topics for consideration:

✓ clear and consistent processes for policy and decision making
✓ levels of staffing and resources
✓ balance of teaching and support staff
✓ support networks, including counselling services, for staff and students
✓ encouragement of staff and student participation
✓ recognition and management of stress
✓ effectiveness of internal communications for students and staff
✓ progress in equal opportunities practice
✓ progress in the practice of student self-supported study
✓ distribution of routine and innovative tasks.

Institutional aspects meriting particular attention

Changing demands
Demands on colleges are changing with increasing frequency, leading to changes of tasks and responsibilities for staff and students. Staff may feel uncertain about their roles, and even doubt whether they have a useful future. It is important to keep job descriptions under review, and to modify and update them with due consultation where appropriate. Closest attention should be given to areas where the impact of change has been greatest. This is vital as college staff members face the implications of corporate status.

Balance of workload
The work of the college is not balanced throughout the year. External changes impose greater workloads on some sections of

the college than on others, and some client groups and sponsors place more demands on college staff than others. Thus pressures on staff may vary by section, and by time of year.

Ethos

Externally imposed planning requirements and demands to meet the needs of different client groups are prime sources of stress. In a period of rapid change the ethos of the college needs to be made explicit and allowed to evolve with the possibility of participation from all staff and users. An example of this situation is the college that needs to move rapidly into a different market, but is failing to consider the needs of its continuing, traditional student groups, and those of the staff who support them.

Support staff

The finding of the project was that many support staff feel that they are not given the consideration and value that they deserve. This emerged from group discussion within a weekly session on prevention and management of stress, attended by a group of support staff. It was further borne out in one-to-one discussions initiated by individual support staff. Hierarchies of status and value should be avoided. Support staff should be given equal opportunities to participate in decision making, and personal and staff development.

A survey can be useful to find out employees' views about their jobs, or about areas of college policy and practice. Group sampling, individual questionnaires and suggestion boxes are all possibilities.

There are also ways to involve support staff in the running and development of the college. Some staff may participate only at times of important change; others may become valuable participants at many levels; yet others will only want an opportunity to express their views periodically and to know these are taken seriously. Dedicating resources to this end is likely to enhance and consolidate change.

Communication

Clear and effective channels of communication between groups and among individuals are features of a healthy organisation. Many of these will be set up formally, others will develop less formally. Channels should be available to transmit, in any direction:

- values
- information
- opinion
- hopes and fears
- ideas
- policies
- objectives.

Informal networks should be viewed positively and supported. Staff support groups – ranging from peer support and 'self-help' groups to inter-professional groups – may be of value to some. Formal networks should be reviewed regularly to ensure that they work well in the face of change. Given the pressure on accommodation, to facilitate constructive networking modifications may be required to the use of space, particularly staff workrooms and meeting places.

Training needs

All staff need an opportunity to examine their skills, knowledge and competence to determine whether they are as relevant and up-to-date as they should be. Not feeling that they possess the competencies which new roles are demanding of them is a key source of stress for staff. There should be a planned and flexible staff training and development structure which should be distinct from the line of management. This is necessary to separate the development and assessment of capabilities to undertake tasks from the assignment and assessment of the tasks themselves.

The project offered short, weekly stress management sessions to students and staff in the pilot college. Initial response from staff was high, but the numbers dropped off rapidly with 'pressure of work' given as the reason. However, a small group of female support staff continued with a weekly lunchtime meeting for the academic year. The group evaluated positively the benefits gained in terms of a greater sense of coping well with stress.

The college curriculum: stress

Changes in method of course delivery

Students who have expectations of a teacher-centred approach may need support in adapting to the demands of self-supported study. This should help them to recognise their own preferred learning style, and to gain from the benefits of being able to use a range of learning strategies. A planned induction is very important, along with a programme of regular progress reviews with each student. Early expectations should be surveyed and monitored at specified points within the course. Follow-up on those who do not complete should include a review of experience, in relation to initial expectations.

Balance of workloads

Modular, assignment-based courses can make conflicting demands on students' time and efforts, especially if programmes are not properly co-ordinated. Inadequate course planning can lead to too many assignments being required within a given space of time. Course teams should ensure that they seek regular feedback from students. Even with a well-developed system for assignments, some students are likely to need guidance in planning and allocating time. If employees and trainees are to meet course demands and achieve the desired outcomes, their sponsors will find it valuable to know in reasonable detail what is being required of them. A structured and systematic programme of reviews is essential to provide individuals with the support that is needed.

Participation

It is also vital for course teams to undertake regular evaluation of their programmes with all concerned, both the students and their sponsors. This provides a check on the quality of the programme from the participants' point of view. Students value constructive channels of communication to course teams and other bodies within the college structure. Colleges can gain much from a regular interchange with students who feel their voices are being heard. It may appear difficult in practice to achieve this. However, time spent developing effective communication channels is likely to pay dividends in the medium and long term. It is likely, for example, to have a favourable impact on retention and completion rates.

Stress management training

The project finding was that there was minimal response from students to either a lunchtime or an end-of-day stress management session. It is more likely that students were unwilling to use their limited free time for such a purpose, or were unaware of the possible benefits of such training, than that they felt themselves without stress, or to be coping perfectly well. It is recommended that tutors consider incorporating some practical work on stress prevention and management into group tutorials or subject sessions, on a trial basis. College staff from physical education and leisure, health studies or counselling services are able to provide the necessary expertise. Alternatively, a local health promotion or education unit might be interested in working on a small trial project (see Chapter 4).

In Figure 9 a second integrated model of health education and institutional development is provided on the topic of stress.

Fig. 9. Stress

Model	Environment	Curriculum	Staff–student relationships	Institution
Health-risk advice	Provide information on the importance of learning to cope with stress.	Provide sessions to raise awareness of stress, and of coping mechanisms.	Ensure that stress is featured in events on such issues as smoking, alcohol and drugs.	Include advice on stress management and prevention in induction programmes and literature for staff and students.
Educational/rational	Identify parts of the environment that may contribute to negative experience, such as poorly equipped toilets.	Explore the causes and manifestations of stress. Practise techniques of stress management and prevention.	Promote extracurricular programmes in stress management and prevention for staff and students.	Ensure that induction programmes for staff and students explore the importance of good time management.
Self-empowerment	Encourage college members to contribute to maintaining a high-quality physical environment.	Develop the skills of stress management and prevention.	Encourage staff and students to expect, and give, respect and consideration from/to each other.	Encourage self-help groups (stop-smoking; women's group; weight reduction).
Action-for-change	Prioritise and schedule a programme to upgrade the physical environment.	Encourage students to plan and participate in a programme on coping with examination pressures.	Review communication channels between staff and students; develop strategies to increase effective communication.	Establish a regular practice of reviewing workloads and job descriptions.

5. Physical activity, fitness and health

The reasons for action

The majority of people in this country lead a sedentary lifestyle associated in part with the widespread use of the car, the reliance on the television for the major part of their leisure time pursuit, and the decline in jobs involving heavy manual labour. This point is well illustrated by the findings of the Allied Dunbar National Fitness Survey 1992. The survey carried out and published by the Health Education Authority and the Sports Council found that even among 16- to 24-year-olds, 70 per cent of men and 91 per cent of women were below the target level suggested for achieving health benefits. This change in lifestyle has dramatically reduced people's daily energy expenditure, and may well contribute towards the increase in obesity. Lack of physical condition can lower resistance to disease, accident or injury. It has been shown that obesity can increase the risk of high blood pressure, coronary heart disease and diabetes mellitus. On the other hand, there are many benefits which participation in physical activities can bring. For instance, it can:

- improve the heart and lung circulation
- help to control body weight
- help to keep the joints supple and alleviate back problems
- tone and strengthen muscles
- relieve some of the effects of ageing
- relieve stress and alleviate pent-up emotions
- increase the body's ability to cope with stress
- give pleasure and bring about a feeling of well-being
- help to increase self-confidence
- increase mental agility
- reduce hypertension in older adults.

The college institution and environment: fitness issues

Fitness facilities

Colleges should consider providing good quality, supervised exercise facilities for both staff and students. Benefits for the college include:

- easing of tensions
- promotion of staff–student relationships
- increase in staff and student morale and self-confidence
- demonstration of the caring attitude of the college
- enhancement of staff–management relationships.

Health awareness and health-related fitness testing

The project used open health-awareness days in each of the three case study colleges to launch the work of the project publicly. The events included staffed displays of health matters. They incorporated testing in stamina, strength and suppleness, following the measuring of height, weight and blood pressure. Testing of this nature was heavily oversubscribed, with staff and students negotiating places.

Demand from staff in two of the colleges led the project to organise health-related fitness testing by appointment over two days. A similar pattern of fitness testing was taken up by most of the participants at the Managing the Healthy College conference for senior managers.

The testing was provided by buying in from health promotion and health education units, and from a local authority leisure centre. Also bought in was the Health Education Authority's Look After Yourself Campaign, now known as the Look After Your Heart: Look After Yourself project (LAYH:LAY), which organises displays, fitness testing and other inputs on a regional basis. Staffing was supplemented in the pilot college by members of the physical education section.

Colleges should investigate the short-term borrowing of equipment, as well as examine the cost-effectiveness of buying equipment themselves. Colleges considering curriculum development aimed at workers in the expanding leisure and recreation industry will need to assess both their resources and their staffing in relation to employer expectations. These expectations may well include the ability to access training in fitness testing across a diverse population (Abbott and Gee, 1989).

Colleges may wish to carry out market research on regular fitness-testing opportunities. In addition, the possibility of taking fitness-testing packages out to local workplaces might be examined.

Guide to good practice

The project fitness open day offered the following positive outcomes:

- ✓ enabling healthy living to be seen as interesting and fun
- ✓ demonstrating the broad scope of health and well-being, emphasising quality of life
- ✓ raising awareness of factors that influence health and well-being
- ✓ opening up channels of communication with local bodies in areas of mutual interest, such as voluntary agencies concerned with special needs.

The Look After Your Heart: Look After Yourself course

In response to a specific request, a recognised LAYH/LAY tutor was used to provide a course for the Youth Training team. This course considers personal lifestyle factors in relation to health such as smoking, diet, physical activity and stress. It examines the way in which work and health interact, and the part which environmental and social factors play in health. The exercise programme takes account of age and existing fitness levels, and is suitable for everyone unless there is medical advice against exercise. Completion of the course opens up the possibility for participants to attend a tutor training course.

Staff who are LAYH/LAY tutors are able to play a major part in promoting health by offering guidance and assistance on health-awareness days, fitness testing and in setting up support groups.

A member of the physical education section followed the course in the pilot college, and then successfully completed the tutors' course. She subsequently delivered a course for staff in one of the associate colleges. The project made this offer in response to demand. LAYH/LAY training may be a useful component of staff development for the expansion of the work of college physical education sections, which is discussed below.

Resources

Space is at a premium in colleges Development and expansion of health-related fitness will need to consider this. It will also need to explore the possibilities within available budgets for staffing, staff training and equipment. Changing and shower facilities should be included.

The college curriculum: physical activity

In past years physical education in colleges did not differ greatly from PE programmes in schools. Students were provided with a sports and recreational service that emphasised performance, frequently in a competitive setting, and which in some places was compulsory rather than optional. From the 1970s, some colleges expanded the traditional role to include pre-vocational courses and health education, and extended their recreation to include community sport.

An FEU occasional paper *Physical Education in Further Education* (Jackson, Neate and Walshaw, 1984) summed up these initial developments as enabling physical education to contribute to the general growth within FE. However, the paper also pointed out that physical education still had '. . . little standing at all, because it is not vocationally viable . . .', and that the '. . . emphasis still appears to be on "recreational" participation . . .' (page 16). The paper goes on to examine the growing demand for the development of vocational courses that meet local and national needs in respect of growth in leisure services, and the scope for future developments.

Possibilities for future work are health-related fitness, and contributions to college activities on personal development and the world of personal activity and unpaid work. Current developments in the core curriculum provide opportunities for this. There is considerable scope for curriculum development in physical education, which is discussed below.

Meeting local needs

Organisations are increasingly becoming aware of the benefits to be gained from paying attention to the health and well-being of their employees. Colleges undertaking resource, curriculum and staff development in relation to physical education may wish to explore the markets for specific health-related fitness programmes in workplaces, as well as offer a community service either within the college or in other community sites.

Provision across the student population

The project finding was that, within the pilot college, the majority of those who took advantage of the fitness facilities offered were young men. Any programme needs also to consider the interests of older men and women of all ages, plus their ethnic identity. The project research showed that young women, especially from Asian backgrounds, were the least likely to participate in any fitness activities.

To encourage these students, the activities need to be fun and relevant, and the programme needs actively to promote some women-only sessions. Many students have been put off sport by school experiences that emphasised performance, competition and compulsion. Many activities included in a physical fitness programme can support group building and co-operation and help to promote the notion that everybody can succeed at being active and gain enjoyment from it.

Physical education sections might offer taster programmes as part of induction courses or as a contribution to group tutorial systems. These can include games promoting trust, developing senses and increasing interpersonal skills. Such activities can be therapeutic in that they help people to relax, to shake off tensions and simply to enjoy themselves. Programmes can include stress management strategies, including relaxation techniques. Links can be made with programmes across the college that deal with personal effectiveness and health skills. Physical education staff need to be involved in the planning of programmes, and in staff development in the areas of groupwork, personal development and health education.

A number of colleges, including the pilot college prior to the project, have included staff from the physical education section in the development and delivery of programmes for students with physical and mental disabilities. Staff development, linked to appropriate regional and national associations, can lead to consolidation and innovation in both separate and integrated provisions for students with special needs.

Vocational courses

Recent curriculum development in relation to GCE A level, BTEC and City and Guilds emphasises practical activities. This thrust is sustained in the emerging framework of GNVQs which will have a significant impact. Resources development may initially be met by in-house expansion or by using existing community facilities. Students may be able to target groups in the college population, as an exercise in investigating client need in relation to fitness issues, and negotiating sessions to meet these needs.

6.   Alcohol and its use

The reasons for action

Alcohol affects concentration, co-ordination and work performance, and if used in excess of the recommended levels for sensible drinking can result in increased absenteeism, sickness and poor timekeeping. This in turn creates problems for those who work with the individual, whether students or staff. The health-promoting college needs to consider the direct and indirect effects of alcohol.

Although the project incorporated the use of alcohol in health-awareness events, and in some curriculum development work, it did not receive as much attention as other health issues. The material in this section, therefore, is derived more from a review of the relevant literature, which includes the development of alcohol policies in workplaces, than from project findings directly.

The college institution and environment: alcohol-related issues

In an institution of even modest size, it is statistically likely that some staff and students will drink too much alcohol. In the absence of clear procedures, colleges often ignore signs of an alcohol problem until or unless events make it imperative to take action. This then tends to be solely disciplinary, and may do little to encourage individuals to seek help. Whether alcohol problems are apparent or not, each college should have an alcohol policy that seeks to cover issues such as the use of alcohol on college premises, dealing with students and staff who have been drinking during college hours, and the provision of alcohol education within the curriculum.

Guide to good practice

The project recommends that colleges consider the following aspects:

- ✓ recognition of alcohol problems
- ✓ the purpose of a college policy on alcohol
- ✓ implementing the policy
- ✓ monitoring.

Recognition of a problem

Many factors contribute to excessive use of alcohol. Often it is a build-up of stress, either at home or at work, that pushes people into relieving the pressure by having a drink. The earlier an alcohol-related problem can be identified and help offered, the better the chance of helping that individual back to full employment or study. These are some of the signs that may indicate there is a problem:

- excessive sick leave; frequent Monday and/or Friday absences
- late returns to work from lunch
- unpredictable mood changes; depression
- alternate periods of high and low productivity
- instability and unreliability
- under the influence of alcohol at work; smelling of

alcohol
- poor co-operation with colleagues
- mistakes owing to inattention or poor judgement
- irritability; over-reaction to real or imagined criticism
- increasingly unkempt appearance; lack of personal hygiene.

No assumptions, however, should be made that alcohol is the key factor.

The purpose of a college policy on alcohol

There are two main objectives. Firstly, a policy can help to promote a sensible drinking message. Secondly, it can develop clear guidelines on alcohol use within the college.

Guide to good practice

Preventive action should include:

- ✓ promoting general well-being by managing and reducing stress in the working environment
- ✓ providing non-alcoholic drinks at functions and in college bars
- ✓ enable staff and students to assess the risks of exceeding recommended limits for sensible drinking, and to consider their own practice
- ✓ make it clear that drinking at lunchtime or evening classes is not acceptable.

An open process for the formulation of the policy can inform and educate as well as involve college members. The support and involvement of the students' union and the trade unions and professional associations of staff will be crucial in attaining the two goals.

The college policy should be clear on confidentiality, job security, sickness benefits and time off for treatment. For students, completion of course work and assignments, position on the course and confidentiality should be clarified. If any of these are not taken into consideration, the individual may feel threatened by fear of dismissal from course or job. All staff and students should receive a clear statement of the policy and its procedures.

Implementing the policy

The college will need a strategy and organisation for carrying out preventive activities. A senior college manager should be designated responsible for implementing and monitoring the alcohol policy, and should work with the college counsellor(s) and any other designated staff. These key people must have training. The programme should cover:

- information about sensible use of alcohol
- development of skills in health education and in identifying alcohol-related behaviour
- appropriate counselling skills
- knowledge of and contact with national and local agencies that can provide assessment and counselling.

The college should advise and support members with an alcohol problem, and actively encourage them to seek help and treatment. It may be possible for colleges to run in-house counselling for staff and students who need help in controlling their drinking. However, many staff and students may find it difficult to accept help from colleagues and lecturers, and may prefer to go to an appropriate agency outside the college.

The strictest confidence between the college team, treatment agency and member of staff or student should be kept at all times. This may need to be done while reassuring college members affected by the problem that the matter is not being ignored, and ensuring that they also receive any practical support necessary.

Remedial action may involve a period of sick leave, and may be characterised by uneven development with some relapse. The college needs to consider the extent of its support and whether practical assistance with workload is desirable.

When guidance is not accepted and the drink problem continues to affect the individual at work, the matter may have to be dealt with under disciplinary procedures. Full involvement of the relevant union and professional associations is vital in determining when disciplinary procedures should be invoked. The procedures should be clear to all members of the college.

Monitoring

It is essential that the policy is monitored at a senior level with union involvement. A survey of staff and students may be useful to assess whether the policy has made any difference to attitudes towards drinking and awareness of personal drinking habits.

The college curriculum: alcohol

Among young people the use of alcohol is frequently a greater problem than use of substances. As with smoking, health education that is restricted to providing information on health risks will be limited in its effectiveness in achieving behaviour change.

Colleges need to explore integrating personal effectiveness and health-skills programmes into their courses. These should enable participants to develop the skills needed to make value judgements and to establish control over their own lives.

Guide to good practice

The project recommends that health education within courses should help people to:

✓ assess the alcohol content of drinks
✓ examine the effects of alcohol on the body and behaviour
✓ explore the role of alcohol in social intercourse
✓ analyse the social and economic interests involved in alcohol
✓ develop and practise skills in managing alcohol consumption
✓ try relaxation techniques
✓ explore possible relationships between alcohol use and unsocial behaviour.

These objectives can be pursued within group tutorials or within existing programmes of learning.

7.   Use of drugs and solvents

Substance use relating to drugs and solvents represents an important, sometimes priority, issue for the health-promoting college. However, given the pre-existing substantial programme of drugs education activities in Birmingham, it was inappropriate for the project to use its limited resources in this area. For city colleges, attention to the use of substances and other drugs was less of a priority than smoking and alcohol because:

- under the auspices of the DES Education Support Grant on Drugs Education, Birmingham LEA had developed a unique, well-resourced drugs education project that has provided support, guidance and training across all phases of education, together with those agencies within the wider community that come into contact with young people
- before the start of the project, college counsellors had identified the use of alcohol as a greater problem
- a major national programme to reduce smoking among young people was being planned.

The project therefore decided to focus on smoking and to some extent alcohol which, although legal, are in human and economic terms more costly, and often more immediate and relevant to the post-16 population.

Summary

This chapter detailed suggestions on ways in which health education and health promotion activities can be developed and integrated into a college setting. The project experience is used to illustrate this process. The chapter identifies seven specific health topics which pose a particular threat: diet and healthy food choices; smoking; HIV/AIDS and sexual health; stress; exercise and health-related fitness; alcohol; and drugs and solvents. Through a discussion of each topic, the chapter presents and comments on a variety of organisational strategies and health education approaches. Wherever possible, it offers guidance on good practice. The chapter proposes an active learning model and relates this to recent curriculum developments in FE.

Health in further education project: case studies of colleges

2

Background to the project 6

The case studies in the second part of this report describe Health Education Authority initiatives in seventeen colleges of further education, from April 1990 to March 1991. The idea of working alongside colleges in this way came from the Tailor Made Training project team's previous experience. It seemed that, in working with further education, more attention needed to be paid to continuing support for staff involved in health education initiatives, and serious consideration given to the context in which they operate. Opportunities for promoting health and health education needed to be identified and the project team therefore proposed to work closely with several colleges over a year.

Through Health Education Authority funding, the project offered:

- a two-day residential course in March 1990. Two members of staff from each college would be invited to attend, in order to draw up an action-plan relevant to their particular situation and needs. The project would meet the cost of accommodation and of the facilitators.
- a day workshop each term, for the group to get back together to share ideas and offer continuing support.
- consultancy. One person on the project team would act as 'consultant' to each college, offering approximately two days' support each term – for the college to use as they saw fit.

In return, each college was asked to provide:

- the release of two members of staff, to attend the residential course, workshops and any working parties, to organise the implementation of a health education

initiative in the college and to write up the case study
with the support of their project consultant.
- travel expenses of the two members of staff.

Introductory residentials

The residentials at the beginning of the colleges' involvement in
the project served two purposes – a getting together with others
engaged in similar work, and a getting together in order to
clarify ideas. The residentials began in similar ways, with
relationship building. This was followed by an outline of the
aims of the two days:

- to clarify exactly what participants were going to do
  given the current resources and time
- to discuss the opportunities for health education in FE
  and tertiary colleges
- to share and learn from experiences in different colleges
- to identify what support participants needed
- to meet the team member who would be offering
  support and consultancy.

The programme on each residential varied slightly according to
the needs of the group, but there were several common
elements. These included:

- different ways of introducing health education,
  including the use of photographs and collage
- the management of change – both personal and
  organisational
- a problem-solving exercise, where participants worked
  in threes on a specific problem back at work, concerning
  health education
- action planning
- evaluation of the two days.

The written evaluation comments were very positive, with
particular mention made of the session on problem solving and
on the usefulness of having time to make action-plans. Most
participants left with a more clearly defined set of objectives and
were clear about the next steps to be taken.

Starting the projects

The first step for most co-ordinators on returning to college
following the residential course was to write a report of their
experience and to submit a proposal for action in the college.
In the main participants were left to decide on the way forward.
The summer term for many consisted of consulting with
colleagues, floating ideas and checking what resources were
available. It seemed a very slow process at times. With
hindsight, this stage was important in getting support from
within the college.

Funding

One of the main difficulties encountered was negotiation over
funding. This was sought mainly for remission from teaching,
for staff development, and for materials and resources. In the
event, co-ordinators found themselves working under varying
conditions. In reading the case studies which follow, this should
be borne in mind. Funding came from a variety of sources, the
most frequent being the TVEI budget and financial support for
the LEA, usually under the Local Education Authority Training
Grants Scheme (LEATGS) (DES, 1989) and later the Grants for
Education Support and Training (GEST) (DES, 1990), where
health education was identified as a priority.

Working parties

Five of the colleges formed cross-college working parties.

In some cases, the working party was set up to encourage the
development of the college as a health-promoting community.
The aim was to represent the whole college, with members from
administration and support staff, as well as academic staff. This
was thought crucial in drawing up policy documents which
could affect all staff and students. Only one working party had
student representation, although others commented that they
were keen to involve students in the future.

Membership of the working parties ranged from eight to nineteen people, including the following:

- the vice principal/deputy director
- college teaching staff – representing different divisions/schools
- student services
- head caretaker
- health and safety co-ordinator
- student union representatives
- youth worker
- college nurse
- administrative officer
- chief technician
- deputy catering manager
- local health promotion officer
- advisory staff for personal, social and health education.

Other working parties were concerned with issues such as curriculum implementation, and more specific tasks, for example, exploring the causes of staff stress.

Several colleges formed small steering groups, often with representation from senior management and LEA advisers.

The cross-college working parties were invaluable in involving staff from different sectors, in raising awareness about health promotion and in offering support to the co-ordinators. Because they were cross college, they also helped to improve communication between divisions and to shed light on differing needs.

The strategies used

The initial brief of the project was to support a range of strategies to promote health education in further education, and colleges were selected with this in mind. As the work progressed, the co-ordinators frequently had to reassess their original plans in the light of discussions on their feasibility. Nevertheless, a wide range of strategies was implemented which included: setting up structures, such as working parties and policies; running awareness-raising events; delivering health education in tutorials; through the induction programme and through the introduction of TVEI; running pilot schemes integrating health education into various courses; setting up a resource centre and surveying the causes of staff stress. The great majority of these involved some form of staff development.

Key learning points

It has been possible to identify certain factors that seem crucial to the success of health promotion in colleges.

The appointment of co-ordinators
Some colleges already have a member of staff with responsibility for co-ordinating health education. This seems essential if this work is to be treated seriously. The co-ordinators need to have sufficient status and to have remission from teaching. It is useful if they have access to the academic board, and are able to put items on the agenda. It is work which needs a level of commitment and interest – and an ability to listen and motivate others. The work benefits from the support of a team.

Support from senior management
More than any other factor, the success of the initiative depended on the support of senior management. Practical support included:

- taking overall responsibility for the project, including attending relevant meetings
- discussions with the co-ordinator on the feasibility of various strategies
- securing funding, for example, to pay for remission
- chairing cross-college working parties
- stressing the importance of health promotion in communications to staff, and providing a response to the cynics
- giving recognition for work done.

The support of senior managers often depended on the merits of a health education initiative, relative to the priorities of the college.

Cross-college support

If the intention was to implement strategies which affected the whole college, for example, through developing smoking policies or considering how much health education could form part of every student's entitlement, it was essential to involve as many people as possible, including all the many support staff working on the various sites as well as the teaching staff. Forming a cross-college working party helped in this, as did surveys to elicit staff and students' viewpoints. Awareness-raising events were also considered important to keep health promotion on the agenda.

It was considered essential to base work around the needs and interests of the students, and wherever possible engage their energy and creativity in the process. Although students on health and caring courses are often engaged in surveys and work which involves other students, there is much untapped potential in integrating health into other courses, for instance, working with students on computing, to help carry out surveys; or with drama students to support health education through the theatre. For most colleges, however, the first stumbling block seemed to be overcoming staff resistance, so that tended to be the focus for the project.

Receiving external support

A day workshop was provided each term for the college co-ordinators, to share the progress that had been made and to gain support in dealing with difficulties. Particular areas covered were strengthening support systems, assertiveness, dealing with 'resisters' in college, team building and reframing negative beliefs.

Throughout the project, co-ordinators found it valuable to meet staff from other colleges, to exchange ideas and renew motivation. Networking was felt to be very important.

All participants commented positively on the benefits of belonging to a national project, funded by the Health Education Authority, and of having access to an outside consultant.

Setting realistic targets

It was considered important to set realistic targets for change over a limited and clearly defined timescale.

'There was a sense of achievement in seeing something through in the time set and within the budget allocated' is a typical comment.

Getting 'health' on the agenda

Co-ordinators who had senior management support were able to set up structures to foster the development of a 'health-promoting college'. This usually meant a working party and health education policy, endorsed by an academic board. It was important that the policy was implemented and monitored, and that changes occurred as a result.

One of the main difficulties facing co-ordinators was overcoming resistance to health education from staff. It was important to recognise the needs of different groups, to gain a greater understanding of their concerns and priorities, and to structure developments so that health education could be seen to be supporting their priorities rather than as an added burden.

Other initiatives vie for time and attention. However, many of these support a broader educational experience for students. TVEI, core skills, entitlement and Records of Achievement are all encouraging colleges to look more closely at their provision of personal and social education. Rather than competing for attention, it seems more effective to collaborate with these initiatives, to show the contribution that health education can make to personal development and effectiveness. Health education is more than giving information about health issues; it also involves developing self-esteem, and interpersonal skills. Staff in the health and caring divisions and in student services often have expertise that is useful in considering a broader curriculum. One first step is to ensure that someone with experience of health education methodology is represented on appropriate working parties.

Another strategy is to keep health on the agenda, by organising awareness-raising events, such as a no-smoking day; by establishing a centrally located resource base, where staff and students can access materials and information about health issues; by infiltrating meetings such as those of programme managers or the health and safety committee, to promote a wider view of health education and to encourage them to take it seriously.

Based on its experience in working closely with the participating colleges, the project team would endorse three principal strategies which were identified at the XIV World Conference on Health Education in Helsinki (Dhillon and Tolsma, 1991):

Advocacy – to heighten public awareness and interest and to impel societal forces that influence public policy and resources to support health.

Empowerment – to help people to develop knowledge and skills to make positive health choices and the ability to act individually and collectively to improve health.

Support – to foster healthful norms, alliances and systems that are sensitive and responsive to the health needs and concerns of the people.

When those responsible for health education programmes act within the context of these three fundamental principles, they maximise their chances of achieving the goal of improved health and quality of life.

Guide to good practice

Questions to ask:

- Is there support from senior management, from the academic board, from the governors?
- Where will you get the funding to buy resources, run INSET, etc?
- Has adequate time been allowed?
- Can you share the responsibilities with a team?
- How will you get cross-college support?
- What are the issues that are important for your institution? Do you know the priorities for management in the college development plan? Is there any link with health education/promotion? Examples might be core entitlement, core skills, TVEI, the tutorial system.
- Where can you get support and contact with other colleges or institutions? Networking is important.
- Can you get support from outside agencies, such as the health promotion/education units?

- Has anyone else done anything similar – in another college, or in industry?
- What is happening already? Have you carried out any form of audit or needs analysis? How can you identify and value good practice?
- How will you consult with staff and students to decide what would best meet their needs?
- Do staff have differing levels of awareness and therefore differing needs?
- Do you need to target certain groups of staff or students?
- Can you involve management, teaching and non-teaching staff, students and outside agencies?
- Can you pilot activities before committing the college to a larger project? This would provide a firm foundation on which further work can be based.
- Can you identify the benefits for staff of becoming involved in the project? Can the project do more for their personal health? With so many changes occurring in post-16 education and colleges generally, staff morale can be low.
- How will you encourage staff to value personal as well as the academic development of students?
- What skills are needed by staff and students?
- What support networks do *they* need?

A detailed report on the background to the project is available on request from Tailor Made Training, 240 Swanwick Lane, Lower Swanwick, Southampton SO3 7DA.

Name of college	Main strategy
Accrington and Rossendale College	Through induction programme – core team of committed people
Chesterfield College of Arts and Technology	Pilot scheme – health education in hairdressing and beauty therapy
East Warwickshire College	TVEI, Records of Achievement
Exeter College	Awareness-raising events
Halton College of Further Education	Health education resource centre Staff development on resources
Henley College	Health education in BTEC courses – initially methodology in BTEC Health Studies
Knowsley Community College	Awareness-raising over importance of personal, social and health education through staff development (including management)
Nelson and Colne College	Pilot scheme – health education in tutorials in consolidation GCSE courses
North Cheshire College of Further Education	Setting up structures: health promotion working party and college health policy

Name of college	*Main strategy*
Northumberland College of Art and Technology	Rolling programme of staff development to deliver health education through tutorials
North Warwickshire College	Student materials for tutorials
Otley College of Agriculture and Horticulture	Raise awareness of staff through support of a health education team Health education in student/staff handbook
Redbridge College of Further Education	Student-centred learning styles plus health education processes as part of the entitlement curriculum
Richmond-upon-Thames Tertiary College	Setting up structures: health education working party and health education input into core curriculum
Sandwell College of Further and Higher Education	Awareness-raising Health Fayre week
South East Derbyshire College	Health education co-ordinating committee Structures in place to support a health education programme Health education policy Health week
Stockport College of Further and Higher Education	Survey into causes of stress for staff

College case study exemplars 8

Accrington and Rossendale College

1. Background

This multi-site tertiary college serves the immediate area around the small industrial towns of the East Lancashire boroughs of Hyndburn and Rossendale. The college also draws many students from the mainly agricultural area of the Ribble Valley, north of Accrington.

Seventy-five per cent of the 1800 full-time students are 16- to 19-year-olds, who are mainly studying on A level and vocational courses, particularly BTEC National Diplomas. There are more female than male students and 14 per cent of the full-time student body is composed of students of Asian origin.

The college's well-developed student services operation is represented at a senior level in the management structure by a Head of Student Support Services and a Senior Tutor (Students). As part of the induction process, all students receive and sign a student contract which makes clear that the college will provide facilities to enable them to complete their course successfully, and that they are expected to undertake, as their side of the agreement, such things as attending classes and completing assignments on time.

Following a successful two-day INSET HE for Tutors held in 1989, a small core group of staff committed to health education was formed. These staff included some elements of health education within the curriculum for their own student groups.

2. Planned outcome

- To provide a health education session within the induction programme for each first-year student starting college in September 1990.

3. Management/staffing

Two LI lecturers who worked on different campuses of the college, were invited to accept responsibility for the day-to-day project management. Overall responsibility was taken by the Senior Tutor: Students and Staff Development. The project came under the remit of the Vice Principal, Curriculum.

No time was allocated to the co-ordinators for management of the project and initially there was confusion over the amount of financial support which the college could provide. The County Adviser for Health Education allocated funding for the college co-ordinators' attendance at the project residential course, and also at the follow-up days each term in London.

During the summer term 1990 details of the budget became clearer and this proved sufficient to cover a two-day non-residential course on health education for 14 people.

4. What they did

After the initial project residential course the two co-ordinators presented a written proposal to the senior management team who gave their approval for implementation.

A two-day course was planned on Health Education in the Induction Programme. The aim of the training was to help tutors plan a one- to two-hour health education session to be delivered to student groups within their own department during the induction period.

It was hoped that the induction programme would 'flag' HEALTH as a priority for the college and convey a psychological message that, *'we are interested in your personal development as well as providing you with appropriate education.'*

The needs of the participating tutors were identified as:

- to experience some student-centred, participatory methods in relation to health education
- to have access to a variety of resources

- to have time in departmental groups to plan the session for inclusion in the induction programme.

The training was advertised in the college bulletin which is disseminated to staff on each of the seven college sites. The advertisement evoked much interest, although in the event many of the interested people did not attend the subsequent training course. Before committing themselves staff were seeking assurance on the funding available and the extent to which the college would support tutors through the dissemination phase. There were also other pressures which inhibited recruitment, particularly the imminence of Local Management of Colleges and the anxiety and insecurity this caused.

One of the co-ordinators submitted her notice at the end of May. It was decided that she would withdraw from involvement in the project on completion of the proposed training course.

Meanwhile a County Steering Group was set up by the Health Education Adviser, to support the case study work in the two Lancashire colleges. At the first meeting it proved impossible to pursue issues related to finance, remission and management support without the presence of representatives of the respective management teams. They were therefore invited to join the group at a further meeting two weeks later.

The two-day training course in June was jointly facilitated by the two co-ordinators and their consultant. Fourteen staff from five college sites attended the training and each made a commitment to include health education in their work with students either through the induction programme or as part of their continuing work.

This enhanced 'task force' met during November, to share their experiences and give mutual support. Most people had found the training very stimulating and were pleased with the resultant health education sessions they had run. Three of the staff, including the project co-ordinator and the Senior Tutor, had been involved in running sessions with student groups from several different courses. This extension of their normal contacts had proved beneficial to the staff as well as the students.

In October the Steering Group held its third meeting and received a progress report from each college. Accrington and

Rossendale College was complimented on the success of its induction programme and the Health Education Adviser decided to send a letter of congratulation to the Principal.

During the spring term 1991 the student and staff evaluation forms were distributed to all tutors who had been involved in introducing health education via the induction programme. However, owing to pressure of other commitments these were used rather sporadically. Only a small number were actually returned and the co-ordinator was unable to draw any conclusions from such a limited sample.

5. Achieved outcomes

- A high proportion of the new students received some health education during their first half term at the college.
- The 'task force' was consolidated.
- Greater awareness of a student-centred, broad-based approach to health education was achieved.
- The above points contributed to a longer-term effect on the college-wide response to such specific events as World AIDS Day.
- The co-ordinator has run a two-day training course for another Lancashire college on health education for tutors.

Future plans

- To offer the Health Education for Tutors course to other Lancashire colleges.
- The 'task force' will continue to operate using hours from Student Services time.
- The media studies team has requested a two-day health education course in the new academic year, to be run by members of the 'task force'.
- The college is to be involved in a further health education initiative being promoted by the County Advisory Service. This project will focus attention on transition management for students, particularly during the move from school to college.

6. On reflection

- The resource implications of any new project need to be thought through and negotiated prior to its implementation. For example, if management support is stated, how that support will be demonstrated in very practical terms needs to be discussed and agreed.
- Need to link more closely with other high profile initiatives in the college, for example, TVEI.
- In order to encourage staff involvement and to provide a response to the cynics, any new project needs an advocate from senior management.
- It might have been more effective to restrict the induction project to events on one college site, evaluate, create a model and then expand to the other sites.

Contact name: Ann Pilkington   Tel: 0254 393521
Address: Accrington and Rossendale College, Sandy Lane, Accrington, Lancashire BB5 2AW.

Chesterfield College of Technology and Art

1. Background

The college is situated near the centre of the small market town on the edge of Derbyshire's border with South Yorkshire. The main student population is drawn from within a 15/20-mile radius of the college, although several of the specialist courses attract applicants from throughout the country.

Of the 2000+ full-time students approximately 80 per cent are aged 16–19 years. The college is making a positive attempt to attract more mature students, particularly women, by the provision of such courses as Women into Management, and Counselling Skills and the Development of Learning.

Derbyshire County Council has long had a policy on positive health education and in 1989/90 the Education Committee identified 'health' as a local priority area, and allocated resources accordingly.

The Student Counsellor/Health Education Co-ordinator at the college ran a very successful Health Week during the autumn term 1989. Given a long 'lead time' many lecturers had involved their students in health-related projects which were displayed throughout the week, as part of the exhibition in the main college hall. This event raised awareness within the college. It was felt that joining the project would support the continued development of health education across the curriculum.

2. Planned outcomes

- Provision of health education for all full-time students through the tutorial system
- Provision of staff development to promote and support the health education initiative (initially in targeted sections)
- Recognition and support for health education and the project by senior management through the provision of time/funding.

3. Management/staffing

The two people initially identified to co-ordinate the project were the Head of Student Services and the Student Counsellor/Health Education Co-ordinator. Both had been involved with the previous awareness-raising work and had a strong commitment to the development of health education within the college. However, owing to the pressure of other work the Head of Student Services was unable to become actively involved in the day-to-day running of the project although he continued to give his personal support.

His place was taken by a lecturer from the special needs department who was keen to introduce health education as part of the curriculum for all her students.

Initially there was no budget, or time, allocated by the college although the county provided cover and travel for the co-ordinator's attendance at both the project residential course and the termly follow-up days. This changed in September 1990 with the provision of four hours per week remission shared amongst the project co-ordinators.

4. What they did

After returning from the residential course the co-ordinator wrote a report describing the experience and outlining the ideas for the development of health education within the college. This report, designed to raise the awareness of the senior management team, was presented to the Academic Board by the Head of Student Services.

Much time was spent discussing ideas with colleagues and trying to form a cross-college health education team. This met with little enthusiasm from the staff. It was proving to be a very difficult time generally for the college. Internal reorganisation was under way with predicted cuts both in budget and in course hours. It also seemed likely that student numbers would fall in some sections in the following academic year and that the tutorial hours were likely to be reduced. An added complication was that for the whole of the following academic year (1991/92) the college counselling service would be reduced from three to two counsellors, thus increasing the responsibilities of the project co-ordinator.

It was against this backcloth that the decision was made to rethink the plans for developing health education in the college. It was decided to focus on developing work within one section, to use this as a pilot, with evaluation built into the initiative, and to bid for more time and money to extend across the college at a later point.

After a further round of consultations with interested staff a lecturer in the hairdressing and beauty therapy department agreed to pilot the introduction of health education through the tutorial programme within her section. She was allocated three hours per week remission to conduct the pilot programme.

Autumn 1990 was the term of many meetings, including individual meetings with all the staff members in the division, to introduce the idea of personal, social and health education and to enlist their support. As a result of these discussions, it became clear that any resources used would have to be written in accessible, easily understood language. Moreover, students had to be able to see the relevance of health education to their course and their chosen career.

With this in mind, the co-ordinator spent time researching books and packs, before writing some sample exercises for tutors to try out either in groupwork or with individual students. The materials were written around the following themes: Career planning, Working in a group and Stress.

In order to raise staff awareness and to help identify elements of personal, social and health education which might already be covered in lessons, a simple checklist was designed and discussed at the regular meetings of the team.

This careful process occupied the whole autumn term as it was felt important to get things right before introducing the ideas to students. Meanwhile, other work was taking place. After some sustained effort the Special Needs Lecturer was successful in getting one hour per week, timetabled from September, for health education with her student groups. The Health Education Co-ordinator had also been busy planning another Health Week. However, while preparations were still in the early stages the authority was poll tax capped and expenditure became limited to absolute essentials. The Health Week was cancelled. During the spring term 1991, staff from the hairdressing and beauty therapy department used the materials with students. Each member of staff spent approximately two hours of tutorial or lesson time working through each of the three packs. The co-ordinator spent time talking with, and supporting, staff as they progressed through the work. She kept notes of all their comments, difficulties, fears and any work undertaken as a follow-up.

On completion of the pilot work, staff and students filled in specially designed evaluation forms, which were returned to the co-ordinator for analysis. It seems clear from the analysis that staff found the packs useful, easy to follow and to work with. The Stress pack seems to have been received favourably by staff and was said to have generated most interest amongst their students. One group followed up their interest by discussing aspects of counselling while another group moved on to look at relaxation techniques.

The evaluation sheet feedback from students was a little disappointing; although 75 per cent felt that they had average to high involvement in the discussions, only 30 per cent reported having enjoyed the work and 20 per cent thought that it had been of some benefit. This may be partly explained by the fact that many students appeared to have covered the topics at school, and that the examples given in the packs related to hairdressing while the students were mostly groups from beauty therapy courses.

5. Achieved outcomes

For the college

- Materials have been produced for use with specific groups of students in the Hairdressing and Beauty Therapy section. These are being refined following feedback from students and staff.
- Becoming involved in the pilot has led to more open discussion at team meetings for the Hairdressing and Beauty Therapy course tutors.
- The health education team in the college was strengthened.
- All full-time students in the special needs department now enjoy one hour per week health education as part of their timetabled curriculum.

For the co-ordinators

- They are much more aware of their own role in the classroom. In the past there was a tendency to be very involved in the subject matter, whereas they now stand back slightly from the subject and think more about the role of facilitator.
- Greater confidence in health education. When the lecturer from hairdressing and beauty therapy first joined the project she voiced her anxiety about the negativity she would meet from her colleagues. On reflection, she realised that she had identified her own fears about health education. Having addressed them helped her to negotiate with her colleagues and also to design materials to address similar fears or negativity from students.

Future plans

- The current materials need to be adapted for wider use.
- Continued research and development to identify the evolving needs of student groups. Further materials will then be written to meet these expressed needs.

Dissemination to other sectors of the college is planned once the present work is consolidated.

6. On reflection

- In an ideal world the work in personal, social and health education needs to be incorporated into the practical work sessions for hairdressing and beauty therapy students, so that it relates entirely to the environment they will eventually find themselves working in. However, it is not clear how this can be achieved owing to the reduction in course teaching time and the extremely time-consuming assessment methods the examining boards are now using.
- Some staff worked with great enthusiasm and obviously felt comfortable with these methods. Other staff found it hard to adopt this approach with its greater focus on discussion and more open-ended methods. Starting the initiative halfway through the academic year made life a little more difficult. People are always happier to introduce new topics, or methods, in September.
- If it had been possible to offer staff appropriate induction by running in-service training around the materials and methods, the initiative might have produced better results.

Contact name: Edgar Riley   Tel: 0246 231212
Address: Chesterfield College of Technology and Art, Infirmary Road, Chesterfield, Derbyshire F41 7NG.

East Warwickshire College

1. Background

In 1990 East Warwickshire College in Rugby had approximately 500 full-time students and 10 000 part-time, most of whom were over 21. The student population was equally split into male and female, and mainly working class. The more advantaged classes in the 16–19 age group tended to go to the grammar or public schools.

A particular strength of the college was engineering and technology for those in employment. In these and other career-related courses health education tended to be treated rather narrowly in terms of the avoidance of accidents and industry-related illness rather than the promotion of health.

TVEI was to be introduced into the college in September 1990. There was commitment in both the TVEI and 1990/91 development plans to the promotion of health education as part of the enrichment of the whole curriculum.

2. Planned outcomes

- To promote personal, social and health education through TVEI and tutorial developments in the college
- In particular, to support staff development in tutor skills and delivering Records of Achievement.

3. Management/staffing

Initially the Vice Principal was responsible for the management of the project at senior level. When he left, it was taken over by the Assistant Principal, with responsibility for TVEI and student services. The implementation was led by the senior lecturer in charge of health and care courses (later promoted to divisional director). She was supported by a member of staff from the same division, who was a full-time lecturer in health studies.

Following the residential course, the two co-ordinators approached the Vice Principal to ask for TVEI hours. They were allocated 72 hours to share between them. However, the heavy tutorial commitments of one co-ordinator meant that she was eventually no longer actively involved in the project.

4. What they did

The co-ordinators talked with colleagues about the place of personal, social and health education within TVEI. Originally they hoped to hold a two-day hotel-based staff development session, for full-time course tutors. However, it soon became clear that, although two days' training in July would be funded through TVEI, this would include only half a day on personal, social and health education. The first day explored the ways in which the tutorial system could support the delivery of TVEI. The morning of the second day was facilitated by the project co-ordinators and explored the skills needed by tutors, with particular emphasis on teaching 'personal enhancement'. The final afternoon consisted of an input by the County TVEI Co-ordinator on Records of Achievement. All sessions seemed to be well received.

In autumn 1990, several changes occurred in the staffing of the college. Amongst those leaving were the Vice Principal and the person with responsibility for the tutorial system in TVEI, while newcomers included a tutorial project co-ordinator, based in the Health and Community Care Training Division. The person acting as project co-ordinator was promoted to director of that division.

The co-ordinators decided to concentrate their efforts on Records of Achievement, as the college was obliged to deliver these from September 1991, and as one of its main purposes was personal development. A TVEI group was formed and a half-day training event was planned to discuss the proposed documentation and completion of the Summative Record of Achievement. This would apply to all full-time students leaving college courses in summer 1991.

The training event finally occurred in January and was repeated the following day to enable as many tutors to attend as possible. There was cross-college representation, mainly LI lecturers, 19 staff in all. The programme, entitled 'Running a Tutorial and Negotiating Records of Achievement – a Skills Approach', used active learning methods. It was successful in helping participants to recognise the work that they were already doing, and the skills they already possessed. One outcome which was surprising was the difficulty for some staff in identifying their own achievements. It increased understanding of the difficulties some students might encounter.

A further half day was arranged in February, and repeated in March, on 'Records of Achievement – the Process and the Product'. Copies of the revised version of the RoA documentation were made available for discussion. All participants had attended either the session in July or one in January.

Meanwhile other health-related initiatives had been taking place. Two staff in Health and Community Care Training had been trying to raise awareness about HIV/AIDS across the college. This included booking a theatre group and organising an HIV/AIDS day for tutors.

The person responsible for the tutorial programme, with the support of a team, is organising monthly optional workshops for students throughout the year. These include health, transitions and careers. Students will be given a pack during induction and can sign up during the year. It will not be compulsory.

The Health and Safety Committee, as in most colleges, had tended to focus on accident prevention and safety. In order to promote a wider view of health, the co-ordinator ran a session on stress for the committee, of which the Principal is a member. The session included defining what is meant by stress, exploring where it comes from and what can be done about it.

5. Achieved outcomes

For the college
It was difficult to separate the project from other work, but the co-ordinator considered that the students were benefiting from increased quality of support, now and in the future. All students will have tutorial programmes and personal tutors with tutorial time. There was increased awareness of the personal and social education needs of students.

For the co-ordinator
The staff development sessions (and the promotion!) increased her confidence. It was good to realise that health and caring courses have been addressing issues that other more academic and syllabus-bound courses are only beginning to take on board. However, she is not complacent as she also came to the conclusion that her own course was not perfect and is looking at ways in which her own students' needs might be better met. It had raised the profile of health and community care training across the college.

Future plans

- Two further sessions were planned, at monthly intervals. The first would address the skills needed in Records of Achievement – interpersonal skills such as respect, empathy and genuineness, listening skills and giving constructive feedback. The second session would discuss the induction programme and how it might support Records of Achievement. Also on the agenda would be the TVEI cross-curricular themes, which include health education.
- It was hoped that the work would be cascaded through the course teams set up throughout the college. The co-ordinator might attend some course meetings herself, putting Records of Achievement, particularly cross-curricular themes, on the agenda and facilitating a session with the team. It has also been suggested that she run a session with divisional directors.
- The team would continue developing the tutorial packages and planning the induction period for students.
- Ideally the Health and Community Care Training Team would offer themselves as consultants, and team-teach across the college. However, other commitments may prevent this.
- Formulating a smoking policy is on the agenda for the divisional directors' meeting and also for the meeting of the Health and Safety Committee.
- Cross-county, a session is planned for colleges to share what has happened as a result of involvement in national projects and to explore possible ways forward.

6. On reflection

- There are several groups meeting in the college with overlapping interest, for example, TVEI, Work-Related Non-Advanced Further Education (WRNAFE) tutorial and Records of Achievement. Some people belong to them all, but not everyone. The co-ordinator was in the TVEI group but sometimes found that she was unaware of what had happened elsewhere. There was sometimes confusion about who was responsible for what. Liaison could be improved and the membership of the groups rationalised.

- Although the choice of co-ordinators seemed appropriate, their other commitments and responsibilities led to an overload of work and difficulty in finding time to meet. It would be better for the second co-ordinator to be someone without too many tutoring commitments. The co-ordinator who had taken on the lion's share of the work was doing it in addition to her job. Although 72 hours were allowed, it was difficult to find the time to fit in the hours! The work needs to be part of the job description.
- The support of senior staff was essential.
- The fact that TVEI is mandatory and funding was available created the opportunity.
- One of the most difficult tasks was getting people to attend the sessions. The issues were still low on some people's personal agendas. It created difficulties in continuity when different people attended each session. Another time the co-ordinator would ask for the Vice Principal's support over releasing certain staff for all the training sessions.
- There is a lot of good practice going on, but little recognition given to staff. How can they help students to identify achievements when they find it difficult themselves? Perhaps it would be better to address the health of the staff before that of the students.
- Involvement in the national project was useful at the beginning, to help to build confidence for the first training session and for access to materials. However, good management support meant that the co-ordinator was not faced with the same problems as in some other colleges, and did not feel the need to seek external help. She thought that the network set up could be useful in the future.
- Using TVEI as a vehicle to introduce issues in personal, social and health education was an appropriate decision. As a cross-curricular theme, a more integrated and subtle approach can be developed in the future. The poor response to the HIV/AIDS training and awareness

session illustrated the lack of support for 'up front'
health education at the present time.

Contact name: Hilary Wright   Tel: 0788 541666 x 3452
Address: East Warwickshire College, Lower Hillmorton Road,
Rugby, Warwickshire CV21 3QF.

Exeter College

1. Background

Exeter College is the tertiary college for the city of Exeter and
the surrounding area, catering in 1991/92 for approximately
2500 full-time and 8000 part-time students.

Following the National Tertiary Survey, the Devon
Curriculum Development Project (DCDP) was established. The
aim was to enlarge and widen the curriculum of all students in
Devon. Health education was included as part of that process.

Within the college, health education was intended to be
included within TVEI but there was not a systematic approach.
An HMI visit in 1989 showed that a health education policy had
not been fully established. As this coincided with contact from
the project, a health education tutor's post was established.

2. Planned outcomes

- To produce a health education policy for the college
- To raise awareness of health issues within the college.

3. Management/staffing

Responsibility for the day-to-day management of the project
rested with the new health education tutor, who was a lecturer
in care studies. She was awarded 60 hours' remission from
teaching time for the first year.

Support was given by the college nurse, who was actively
involved in the project. Senior and middle managers played an
active part in supporting the health education tutor.

4. What they did

The health education tutor decided to raise awareness through organising events, often in conjunction with national 'Health' days.

In the summer term 1990 the college participated in Drinkwise. The event was supported by a wine lecturer, his colleagues and students. Staff and students were involved on the day in activities such as low alcohol/non-alcoholic drinks tasting and a quiz. It was well supported by staff, management and students.

As part of Look After Your Heart there was a stand with leaflets and a display in the main foyer. The Principal was photographed on an exercise bike for the local press!

In autumn 1990 the college arranged a Health Fair for one day on the main campus. The staff involved in the organisation and running of the day were: a health education tutor, college nurse, psychology lecturers, physical education lecturers and the catering department. All first- and second-year tutors were invited to bring their tutor groups, at a specified time. This was effective in conveying a commitment to attend. Heads of school and management were invited and many attended. The day was busy and a wide range of students participated.

As the college received no prior notice of National Aids Week, there was a display only. However, many leaflets were taken by students and others passing by the stand in the main foyer.

In the spring term 1991, a short session was organised for staff, entitled 'Sex, Drugs and Rock 'n' Roll'. The aim was for tutors to meet the doctor who comes into college once a month, to discuss how they might make the best use of her time. She was willing to go into tutor groups, or to see individual students. Despite a low attendance, the tutors found the session useful.

On No Smoking Day in March 1990 'Sir Walter Raleigh' visited the college by courtesy of the Health Promotion Department. Cigarettes were discarded for a baked potato. The day was well supported by management who changed an advertisement for posts to 'Non-smokers preferred' (*Times Educational Supplement* of 22 March 1991). The event was covered by radio, TV and local press.

The health education tutor also re-formed a cross-college working party, which now meets approximately once a term.

The in-house magazine, *Round Up*, is used by the tutor and working party to advertise forthcoming events.

5. Achieved outcomes

The profile of health education has been raised and most staff are aware that help is available from a variety of means: personal, resources, events and workshops. For the health education tutor the project has been a welcome extension of her work.

Future plans

It was proposed that the post be awarded 90 hours' remission time from September 1991, in order to be increasingly effective. Staff workshops are planned. The health education tutor has been invited on to two college committees and feels generally well supported. She also intends to meet tutors and their groups.

Tutors and management have been very encouraging in their support of health education activities. This has mainly been in their active participation in organised events. Work is progressing with the welfare committee, chaired by the Assistant Vice Principal, currently developing health policies. Support is given by the local Health Promotion Department and many staff give active support when requested.

6. On reflection

- The real learning is difficult to measure and is inevitably a slow process.
- The post needs more recognition by management.
- The health education tutor feels health education should take precedence over multi-culture by virtue of the population. However multi-culture is a cross college post and so impact can be made on committees. She felt many of her decisions were made in ignorance of management thinking.

Contact name: Pat Boaden   Tel: 0392 383115
Address: Exeter College, St James's Annexe, St James's Road, Exeter, Devon EX4 6PU.

Halton College of Further Education

1. Background

Halton College of Further Education, situated in North Cheshire, has a student population of approximately 1300 full-time and 9000 part-time. Slightly more females enrol than males, and students are predominantly British, white and working class. As in most districts, there are falling rolls, especially in the 16–19 age group, and the college is seeking to attract older age groups, for example, women returners.

Each of the college's five departments has a mix of full-time and part-time students based on sites in Widnes and Runcorn. As a locality Halton has particular health problems. The Halton Health Profile published in November 1990 stated that coronary heart disease is 22 per cent higher for men and 21 per cent higher for women than the national average.

The college runs a Certificate in Health Education course, validated by the Health Education Authority and jointly organised and delivered by college and district health education staff. In 1988 the Academic Board approved the formation of a working party, which conducted health education surveys of all full-time staff and a sample of students in March/April 1989. These showed clearly the desire amongst both staff and students for more activity-based sessions, more curriculum and resource materials to be available for the teaching of health topics, and the need for lecturers to be more fully informed in the delivery of relevant and up-to-date health topics.

2. Planned outcomes

- To establish a resource centre of health education materials for use by staff and, where appropriate, students
- To run workshops for staff throughout the college to publicise the health education resources and their suitability for inclusion into existing courses
- To continue to develop an in-house health education programme for both staff and students.

3. Management/staffing

Two members of staff were directly involved in initiating and
delivering the project. Both had status in the college hierarchy,
one being a Principal Lecturer in Pre-vocational and
Community Studies, and the other Head of Guidance and
Counselling, with a cross-curricular role. No abatement was
sought or provided. Both members of staff have reduced
teaching timetables and were prepared to give time to the
project.

In June 1990 the position on funding was clarified. The LEA
granted the college £1150, of which £650 was to purchase
resources and £500 for related staff development.

4. What they did

The co-ordinators were unable to make headway until they
knew what money was available. At a meeting of the Cheshire
Health Education in FE Liaison Group, the Adviser for
Community and Health Education invited bids under the
Education Support Grant (for further details see 'North
Cheshire College of Further Education'), and the co-ordinators
later heard that their bid had been successful.

Following a visit to the HEA resource library, the co-
ordinators compiled a list of possible teaching materials. They
decided not to purchase videos, but to use the funding on books
and packs, having been advised that teaching packs were the
most accessible way of getting busy teachers to embark on
health education. The resources were ordered for delivery in
September.

They were kept in Student Guidance and Counselling, so that
they were seen as accessible to the whole college rather than just
one department. They were not made available to staff until
after two training sessions of three hours each in November.

A memo was sent to all heads of department, asking for their
support in encouraging staff to attend the training. A publicity
leaflet was circulated to every full-time member of staff. It
contained information about the project, the resource centre
and the dates for the supporting staff development. The
intention was to attract to each training session ten tutors,
representing different departments in the college. The aim of

the sessions was to inform them about the resources and discuss appropriate teaching methods.

Nineteen staff responded although unfortunately they did not represent all departments, coming mainly from Pre-vocational and Community Studies. A further session was requested for special needs staff. This was held in December, with eight participants.

An evaluation form was completed at the end of all the sessions by all participants. Comments were very positive. People appreciated the range of resources. Six participants said that they would use most, if not all, of them. Others identified particular issues or packs in which they were interested.

In response to the evaluations, a further day was organised in February on Active Learning Methods. Twelve people attended, from one college department, and were a combination of health, social care and special needs staff. The majority found the day thought-provoking and informative.

The resource centre has now been set up, with a recording system on the issues of materials. The centre has been publicised in the staff newsletter. It is still largely being used by one department. It is also having a ripple effect, with some sections deciding to buy their own copy of certain packs. As a direct result of the project, a TVEI Working Party has been established to consider using the resources purchased and similar staff training sessions for tutors involved in 32 full-time courses across the college.

Meanwhile other initiatives took place. The Health Education Working Party was asked to develop a sex education policy for the college to present to the Academic Board. Through the County AIDS Co-ordinator, a project has been initiated to involve students in peer-counselling. A group project was set up in November 1990, involving students from the Certificate in Health Education course in identifying the health needs of staff and students within the college. The educational psychologist ran a stress management course for both staff and students, over six weeks, one hour a week.

5. Achieved outcomes

For the college
- a permanent resource centre which has the potential to benefit staff and students alike for many years to come
- a group of staff familiar with the resources
- a greater awareness in the use of interactive methods, through the approaches advocated in the teaching materials. For many staff this has been their first encounter with this particular approach to learning.
- a committee looking at health education in TVEI
- increased interest in health education in special needs.

For the co-ordinators
- the project increased their commitment to health education and expanded their knowledge. They learnt more about active learning methods, which they now use. There was also a sense of achievement in seeing something through in the time set and within the budget allocated.

Future plans

At the moment, one department has benefited more than others, in that the staff involved in the training sessions came mainly from Pre-vocational and Community Studies. In the future the co-ordinators hope to reach staff in other departments through TVEI, making use of the resource base. Two staff development sessions have already been planned, one to examine the packs and another to consider appropriate teaching methods.

Additional funding from TVEI is to be allocated for extending the resource centre. Staff will be consulted before additional resources are purchased. A group of special needs staff are examining ways to develop a health education curriculum module which will be taught from September to all students, full- and part-time within the section. They wish to replicate the project and establish a resource centre containing materials for students with moderate and severe learning difficulties.

It is hoped that the Health Education Working Party will develop a college health education policy to be submitted to the Academic Board. One recommendation is likely to be the appointment of a health education co-ordinator, with a cross-college role and with abatement to organise and develop health promotion initiatives for staff and students. The working party will also examine the issue of no-smoking staff areas.

6. On reflection

- Without county support and money, the resource centre would not have been funded.
- The project was useful in imposing a timescale. It put pressure on the co-ordinators to deliver the goods within the time! It was important to set realistic achievable goals within the time and resources available.
- There were mixed feelings about the County Liaison Group. The idea of a group to share ideas and learning seemed very positive, and county support was much appreciated. However, the focus seemed to move away from developing links and team-building to accountability. It might have helped if colleges could have had more control over the agenda and could have looked for ways of supporting one another.
- The greatest hindrance was the fact that the project depended on the goodwill and energy of the co-ordinators, who had to find time on top of their usual commitments.
- The materials purchased were largely an educated guess. It is already becoming apparent that some will be in great demand, while others will hardly be used. It would have been preferable to consult somehow with staff about their needs, before placing orders. Unfortunately this was difficult within the timescale of the project.
- The biggest disappointment of the project was that it has not reached staff in all departments. There might have been a better response if the co-ordinator had made personal contact with staff, but his heavy workload inhibited this.

- It was crucial to have senior management support, both through the Curriculum Development Group and the Academic Board. It was vital to get the project on the agenda of the Academic Board.
- The co-ordinators were appropriate people for the task. They formed a good partnership, one having a cross-curricular role, while the other had the credibility of being involved in health studies. They were also in a position within the college hierarchy to be able to put items on the agenda of the Academic Board.

Contact name: Dave Trowbridge   Tel: 051-423 1391 x 227
Address: Halton College of Further Education, Kingsway, Widnes, Lancashire WA8 7QQ.

Henley College

1. Background

The college has approximately 1400 full-time, 16–19 students, mainly white and middle class, and 4000 part-time students. Two members of staff had been involved in the HEA 16–19 Developing Training Skills Course. Attempts had been made to develop tutorial packages for use in tutorial time, but staff were reluctant to be involved. It was a time of reorganisation in the college.

2. Planned outcomes

- To explore the areas of health education appropriate to BTEC courses in the college
- To promote student-centred learning through the use of health education and interpersonal skills material.

3. Management/staffing

Two members of staff were directly involved in the project – a part-time assistant lecturer who is the BTEC Health Studies Co-ordinator and a student counsellor. The LEA provided funding to give the co-ordinator remission time of one hour a week.

Further funding was to be available for staff development. The Director of Student Services was responsible for overseeing the project, although the holder of this post changed as the project got under way.

4. What they did

The BTEC co-ordinator in collaboration with the Director of Student Services and the LEA Adviser for Personal and Social Education drew up a list of objectives for the project. This formed the basis of the bid for funding from the LEA.

The objectives were:

(a)   To identify the areas of health education appropriate to the BTEC courses at Henley College.

(b)   To investigate health education material available.

(c)   To produce appropriate packs of student-centred activities for use in the various BTEC courses.

(d)   To facilitate the uptake of the material with support and workshops for staff.

(e)   To obtain the support of the Principal and staff of Henley College for the running of 'active learning workshops' for staff.

(f)   The incorporation of modules into BTEC courses.

(g)   The running of active learning workshops using health education and interpersonal skills material to encourage the use of student-centred learning at Henley College.

Target dates were also set for each objective.

In the event, activity has focused on the BTEC Health Studies Certificate Course and raising awareness of students throughout the college to health issues of importance to them.

The co-ordinator explored how student-centred activities could play a prominent part in the BTEC Health Course. Students have been encouraged to analyse the work they have done, to use a wide range of resources, to comment on the methods, and whether they found them useful. It is hoped to share these experiences with tutors on other BTEC courses by running staff development workshops. Pressure of time has made it difficult to overcome staff resistance.

Several events have raised the profile of health for students. An outstanding example was the Snow-Go Project, organised by students on the BTEC Health Course. Fourteen students with support from their tutor, one of the co-ordinators of the project, undertook to raise £8000 to give special needs students a chance to learn to ski, and the opportunity to be part of a group on holiday. £10 000 was raised so more students with special needs were able to join the group. In the words of the students – 'We were able to feel a sense of satisfaction and fulfilment at what we had accomplished' and 'the unforgettable memories of the holiday will remain with us for ever.'

The two co-ordinators decided to run events which would be directly relevant to students' health needs. They organised an HIV/AIDS questionnaire/quiz to be circulated to all tutor groups. There was a prize of £10 for the tutor group that sent back a complete set of questionnaires. All complete sets were put into a draw. The answers to the quiz were made available the following Monday and students encouraged to go to the room where answers were displayed. Posters, leaflets and other information were available, together with a video of a recent Channel 4 documentary on HIV/AIDS. More than 80 students turned up during the day getting answers to their queries.

A no-smoking day is being organised in conjunction with Comic Relief. Tutor groups can sponsor students to come to a Stop Smoking Clinic. BTEC students have carried out a survey covering:

(a)   Students who smoke and would like to give up
(b)   Those who have given up and how they did it.

The results will be fed back to tutor groups and could form the basis of future work, again based on student needs.

A working party has been set up to look at the tutorial system. Questionnaires are to be circulated to tutors and students concerning TVEI and should lead to further action.

There has also been an investigation of core skills in preparation for implementation within the college. The current debate about core skills/entitlement will help to make links with other staff and courses.

5. Achieved outcomes

For the college

- The whole college has had the opportunity to be involved in health promotion, leading to a greater awareness of certain health issues.
- A pilot study has been conducted into the appropriateness of student-centred activities in the BTEC Health Studies Course.

For the co-ordinators

- A sense of achievement from running successful awareness-raising events within college and gaining positive responses from many students and tutors.
- A recognition of the willingness of students to be involved with health promotion activities.
- Encouragement from areas within college and from parents that it is important for students to develop interpersonal skills.

Future plans

- Input to induction courses, possibly using students.
- Publicising how health education materials can help other courses, for instance, Business Studies.
- The opportunity to run staff development workshops.
- The new Vice Principal is interested in the work and will give it support. There is also continuing support from the LEA Adviser for Personal and Social Education.

6. On reflection

- It helped the co-ordinators to be able to work together to share ideas, boost one another's morale and find ways round the resistance of other staff. It was also useful to meet representatives from other colleges and to find that you are not alone in facing problems.
- The LEA Adviser for Personal and Social Education provided ideas and encouragement, for example, approaching senior management on behalf of the project.

- The project was hindered by lack of time and the apathy of other staff towards any health policy.
- It would have been preferable to obtain the practical backing of senior management at an earlier stage of the project.
- Changes in the course requirements for BTEC led to uncertainty in planning appropriate activities. However, overall, it is hoped to capitalise on discussions about the changes in BTEC, by putting health education and active learning methods on the agenda.
- It would have been better to run pilot activities before committing the college to be part of the project. This would have provided a firm foundation on which work could begin.

Contact names: Pippa Clark or Josephine Thomson
Tel: 0491 579988
Address: Henley College, Deanfield Avenue,
Henley on Thames, Oxon RG9 1UH.

Knowsley Community College

1. Background

Knowsley Community College resulted from the amalgamation of Knowsley Tertiary College, Kirkby Further Education College and some local high school sixth forms. The community college was established in September 1990. At the beginning of the project the Principal had been appointed, but the senior management team was incomplete.

The Director of Education wrote to the project supporting the college's bid to be involved, and pointing out that Knowsley is an area of high social deprivation that has developed over a number of years as an overspill from Liverpool. The area is predominantly unskilled working class, with higher than average unemployment. There are approximately 2200 full-time students and many more part-time students.

Considerable work had already taken place in the borough. Following the national conference on health entitlement, organised by the HEA in 1989, a working party was set up in

Knowsley to produce a statement of entitlement for 16-plus in health education. Membership included the Teacher Adviser for Health Education, and a few staff from the college.

2. Planned outcomes

- To raise the profile of personal, social and health education through staff development
- To develop a whole college approach to health education
- To further the work already begun by the borough working party and to use the expertise developed through involvement in previous projects.

3. Management/staffing

The co-ordinator had been involved with the HEA 16–19 Dissemination Project, attending a developing training skills course in 1986 and the national conference three years later. She was also a member of the borough working party. She was an L1 in biology and health studies.

Unfortunately time and funding were not clarified at the beginning. No time was allocated. Funding for staff development came from the TVEI budget in the college and the LEA.

As the appropriate posts had not been filled when the project was set up, there was no member of the management team with overall responsibility.

4. What they did

The co-ordinator found herself at a disadvantage during the project residential course in that she was the sole representative from her college. On her return, she approached several people in college in an attempt to set up a working party. Although most expressed an interest, there seemed to be a reluctance to do anything until the Assistant Principal, Learning Support was appointed.

Several meetings were arranged involving Knowsley's Teacher Adviser for Health Education and the TVEI Co-ordinator, the project co-ordinator, the college TVEI Co-ordinator, the Senior Lecturer with responsibility for Student Services and the Course Manager for Vocational Courses. This group later became the planning team for the project, and other health-related issues within the college. The project consultant also met the Principal, who promised his support.

The idea was floated to arrange a two-day INSET on health education for a group of interested staff who would then begin to disseminate it in their own divisions. However, differences of opinion arose about the purpose of the INSET and the feasibility of an event for both managers and practitioners. Because of her status as a main grade lecturer, the co-ordinator did not feel she had the power to influence events as she would have wished. This remained a problem throughout.

The final decision was to hold one day on Developing a Policy for PSE in TVEI for managers in the college. The objectives of the day were as follows:

- to clarify the aims of personal development
- to identify the skills involved in personal development
- to identify and discuss models of delivery
- to begin to develop a policy for the college.

The nine participants were the two Vice Principals, the Course Managers for GCSE and Vocational Courses, Senior Lecturers from Special Needs, Careers and Student Support, Knowsley's Teacher Adviser for Health Education and the person with responsibility for TVEI in the borough. The day was organised by the co-ordinator and the project consultant.

The final session involved clarifying the current situation in the college and discussing the way forward. The following tasks were identified:

- to find out what staff were doing already – what is in the curriculum
- to increase awareness about the role of personal and social education
- to form a working party for personal and social education
- to involve quality teams in identifying the needs of students and staff
- representation to governors

- to clarify priorities about resources, for example, time and money.

A follow-up meeting was arranged to discuss ways forward, including the training of quality team leaders and the value of an audit. It was decided that the next step was to target staff in both vocational and GCSE/A level courses, inviting staff who had shown an interest to a day's INSET to raise awareness about work in personal, social and health education. The idea was to have a representative from each subject area.

The day was run in December 1990 with eleven participants – drawn from Sociology/Politics, Psychology, Sciences, Geography, Engineering, Hairdressing, Horticulture and Caring, with support from the borough from the Teacher Adviser and the TVEI Co-ordinator. The aims were:

- to define personal, social and health education
- to identify what is happening now in the participant's subject or area of work
- to suggest what needs to be done in the future.

As a result of the day various recommendations were made about future action, which the co-ordinator fed back to the TVEI/PS-E group and the Principal. However, no time was allocated for the work, so that it was not possible for the co-ordinator to develop this further.

In January the two new Assistant Principals, one for General Education and one for Learning Support, took up their appointments. (The Assistant Principal, Learning Support was previously involved in the health education initiative of another college.) The Assistant Principals arranged a meeting with the Planning Team.

5. Achieved outcomes

For the college
- Personal and social education was kept on the agenda during the developmental stages of the new college
- Links were made with the Teacher Adviser for Health Education and later the Health Promotion Unit
- Managers had the opportunity to review the way in which personal and social education is delivered

- The foundations were set for future developments, now suggested by the new Assistant Principals.

For the co-ordinator

She achieved some personal 'firsts', in arranging and co-facilitating INSET for Vice Principals and managers, and in chairing the TVEI/PSHE group.

She identified supportive staff within the college, and was part of a support network outside.

Her own personal growth involved the development of assertiveness, management skills, a sense of her own self-worth and the ability to let go when necessary so that others 'own' the changes.

Future plans

The new Assistant Principals are building on what has happened in the project to introduce a modular programme in personal, social and health education to enhance A levels and GCSE.

6. On reflection

- Initially it seemed an ideal opportunity to be involved in the development of a new college. However, trying to introduce a new initiative at such an early stage proved problematic. Little could be achieved until the relevant management appointments had been made.
- The co-ordinator was at a disadvantage for a variety of reasons:
  — her LI status within the college. (She found herself chairing and facilitating meetings with college managers, including her own line manager.)
  — the fact that two project co-ordinators were not appointed.
  — the fact that the senior management team was incomplete at the start of the project.
- The co-ordinator welcomed support from the Planning Team, the College Counsellor and Senior Careers Officer.

- A contract should have been drawn up between the co-ordinator and the Principal with regard to the project.
- For the project consultant, involvement with the project was a reminder of the difficulties faced by staff and students in economically disadvantaged areas.

Contact name: Claire Mason   Tel: 051-443 4243
Address: Knowsley Community College, Bracknell Centre, Bracknell Avenue, Kirkby L32 9PP.

Nelson and Colne College

1. Background

Nelson and Colne is a tertiary college, formed from the existing technical college and from sixth forms of partner schools in 1972. The college serves a multi-cultural community in the Pendle District. Its students come from a range of communities, including urban and rural. Approximately 80 per cent of the full-time students are 16- to 19-year-olds.

Some students, particularly those on caring and related courses, receive health education as part of their set curriculum.

The college has a stated commitment to providing a broader, more balanced curriculum for all students and also to enhancing student support through development of the counselling and careers service. The TVEI extension was due to start in the college in September 1990 and the senior management team saw this as an opportunity to move towards the broader curriculum they espoused. Involvement in the project offered the opportunity to explore, on a small scale, some of the options being considered. The fact that the County Adviser for Health Education was offering to support the initiative by providing some financial assistance also contributed to the decision.

2. Planned outcomes

- Health education to be available to all students either as an integrated part of their learning programme or through the personal tutorial system

- Enhancement of the cross-college counselling service.

3. Management/staffing

The Vice Principal assumed overall responsibility for the management of the project and liaison with the County Adviser for Health Education.

The continuing work of the project was undertaken by two members of staff on lecturer grade, both of whom already had heavy teaching commitments. One (an LII) was lecturing in the Business Studies Department and also fulfilled a counselling role for the college, and the other person (an LI) was teaching 22 hours per week in the Science and Engineering Department.

There was some confusion initially over the funding available from external sources. The college was unable to allocate a budget to the project or to provide remission from teaching for the two staff. However, in the latter part of the project cover was provided for a small group of tutors to attend two separate INSET sessions.

The county supported the project by funding travel, attendance at the project residential course and the three support days which followed. Funding was also offered to the project co-ordinators to cover out of college meetings for planning, development, report writing and attendance at meetings of the County Steering Group.

4. What they did

Fired with enthusiasm after the initial residential course, there was a flurry of activity when the co-ordinators returned to the college. This included:

- meetings with the Vice Principal to exchange ideas, discuss plans and implications for funding and to begin the development of a strategy;
- establishment of a cross-college working party by personal invitation and through advertising in the college newsheet. The original intention was to encourage every college department to participate. The working party was eventually formed with

representatives from five of the college departments and a member of staff with cross-college responsibilities;

- a simple questionnaire was designed to assess students' interest in having health education included in their course and to ascertain which specific areas they would like addressed. The questionnaire was used with 84 students who were randomly selected from eight course groups. The results pointed to a definite desire for some health education to be included. There was a need!

Early in June 1990 several meetings took place to review the progress and direction of the initiative and to consider the implications of the information from the questionnaires. It was finally decided that, in view of the lack of time and funding available, a more modest initiative might be preferable. If a complete course team were willing to pilot the introduction of health education in the tutorial system, this could be monitored and evaluated for dissemination across the college. It was also hoped that a department or section might welcome exploring the integration of health education into the course curriculum. This would result in two models of delivery which would afford comparison.

The co-ordinators made a personal approach to several sections to elicit their involvement in the initiative, either through the integration of health education into the course curriculum or via the tutorial system. Although interest was expressed by some members of staff, it was generally felt that tutors were already undertaking major developmental work in providing Records of Achievement and profiling for students. This was the first priority for the college as a whole and tutors could not take on anything additional.

Eventually, after some help from the Vice Principal, tutors teaching on the Consolidation GCSE courses agreed to become involved and to consider introducing health education into their tutorial periods. It proved impossible to locate a course team prepared to look at integrating health education into the existing course curriculum, so this part of the pilot was not pursued. A two-day staff development programme was designed to support the personal tutors taking part in the pilot. This course offered an experiential and broad-based approach to health education within tutorials, including methods, materials and available resources.

Timing of the INSET presented difficulties because of examination commitments and other pressures. It was quite a frustrating period for the two co-ordinators who felt a sense of time running out on them. The two-day course, originally planned for June, was reduced to one day and finally took place in October 1990. The day proved to be very successful; the small group of personal tutors were enthusiastic and some seemed keen to include health education in their tutorials. Several expressed an interest in further staff development to look particularly at 'learning styles' and 'counselling skills', so that a follow-up half-day was successfully run in January 1991.

The Vice Principal and both project co-ordinators were involved in the County Steering Group which was set up to support the development of health in further education in Lancashire. Owing to teaching commitments and the timing of meetings it was rare for more than one representative of the college to be present at each meeting.

In August 1990 as part of the new college structure, and to enhance and co-ordinate the non-teaching services provided for students, the Student Support Unit was established.

5. Achieved outcomes

- Following the two successful INSET sessions a small group of tutors in one learning programme area are including health education in their tutorial programmes.
- This group of tutors are meeting regularly to share experiences, discuss ideas and enhance their skills. The project has also enabled them to adopt new methods and materials in their approach to health education.
- There is a greater awareness of broad-based health education, and its importance for young people, amongst the staff at the college.
- There is a greater acknowledgement of the need to develop a health education policy for all students.

Future plans

- As a result of the last tutors' meeting a Health Promotion Fayre is being suggested for one of the days in student induction week in September 1991.
- A health education resource area situated in the Student Support Unit is being planned.

6. On reflection

- The enthusiasm of the cross-college team/working party provided initial encouragement. However, when the project's aim was changed to a pilot programme working with a small group of tutors, the working party seemed superfluous and it was disbanded.
- The two co-ordinators felt that it was helpful to be involved in a national project which gave them access to an external consultant. They felt supported both personally in terms of acknowledging their achievements and disappointments, and professionally in the planning and running of the INSET, and the provision of ideas and materials. As an 'outsider' coming to the college, the consultant provided status and worth to the project; participating tutors felt it to be worthwhile and meaningful. Also, in the 'outsider' role, the consultant held discussions with the Vice Principal in order to clarify the position and move the project forward.
- Resourcing at the appropriate level, both in time and finance, was necessary from the outset.
- Heavy teaching commitments, the high investment of time spent in making personal contact with people and the reluctance to become involved expressed by staff – all sapped the morale of the two project leaders.
- Suitable opportunities for co-ordinators and/or working group members to meet needed to be identified at the outset of the project. Without these the project co-ordinators tended to feel isolated.
- It would have helped if clear objectives had been agreed at the outset. Confusion over the aims did not help the identification of project co-ordinators, who needed to

have power and responsibility for the project to succeed.
It did not help that, as lecturers, the two co-ordinators
had little or no 'clout' in their negotiations with more
senior members of staff.

- Similarly the project needed to have status and to be
  acknowledged as important by key members of staff.
  Other priorities were given precedence, and the absence
  of the Vice Principal because of prolonged illness made
  the management of the project more difficult.
- Changes in conditions of service owing to Local
  Management of Colleges came into effect soon after the
  project began. This seemingly additional stress factor for
  staff and management raises questions in relation to the
  timing of the national project.

Contact name: John Farrington   Tel: 0282 603151 x 202
Address: Nelson and Colne College, Scotland Road, Nelson,
Lancashire, CB9 7YT.

North Cheshire College

1. Background

The culture of the college is influenced by it being a college of
further, higher, continuing and adult education. At the beginning
of the project there were approximately 1000 full-time students,
with equal male and female distribution. The college has
recently been restructured. Each school has a manager, whose
responsibilities include staffing and timetabling, and formulating
a development programme. There are also programme
managers, operating across schools, who have responsibility for
courses. The college has also formed a separate company, based
on one of the three sites. This has its own board of directors, and
runs profit-making courses for outside agencies.

The School of Applied Social and Health Studies was one of
the largest in the college. Along with other schools it has
reduced staff numbers in recent years.

It was amongst the first colleges to sign the Look After Your
Heart charter, directed mainly at staff. Health education
appeared in the curriculum of caring or health courses but
seemed rarely available to other students. The reason why the

college wanted to participate in the project was to add impetus to the development of a coherent college health strategy.

2. Planned outcome

- To formulate a college health policy which would be the foundation of further health initiatives.

3. Management/staffing

The co-ordinators were both based in the School of Applied Social and Health Studies, one being an LII lecturer and the other a main grade lecturer. Both were experienced LAY tutors, committed to a holistic approach to health.

Initially there was no budget or time allocated for the initiative. However, in June 1990 the college was granted funding of £1000 from the authority for abatement for the Health Education Co-ordinators (a total of 56 hours – 4 hours per week for 14 weeks) and cover for staff attending meetings.

4. What they did

Following the initial residential course a short report was sent to the Director outlining the planned outcomes and mentioning some of the issues causing problems. The main difficulty was uncertainty over the availability of financial support to pay for staff time. One of the co-ordinators wrote the first draft of a health education policy, based on a document from another college involved in the project. This was then discussed at a meeting with the Health and Safety Officer and the project consultant. Consideration was given not only to the wording but also to how to proceed so that more people could 'own' the policy and it stood a chance of being implemented.

A meeting was arranged in May 1990 by the County Adviser for the co-ordinators from the two colleges involved in the project, the County Health Education Co-ordinator and representatives from other Cheshire colleges who had participated in a three-day training programme of the HEA 16–19 HIV/AIDS Project. Feedback was given about the experience on the two projects, and what had happened since in colleges. The LEA informed the group that £2000 was available to further education, through the Education and Support Grant, and invited bids from colleges for health education projects they wished to initiate.

North Cheshire College submitted a proposal, requesting funding mainly for staff remission. Following discussions with the group, the funding was granted.

The next step envisaged was the setting up of a Health Education Cross-college Co-ordinating Group, consisting of approximately eight members of staff, plus the two co-ordinators and the Health and Safety Officer. The intention was to involve staff who normally have no connection with health and would not be seen by the rest of college staff as 'health fanatics'! The meetings would raise awareness of health issues, act as a sounding board for ideas and be a forum for discussion. It was also considered important to have the visible support and attendance of senior management. The Deputy Director agreed to be the designated senior manager and to chair the meetings. He was concerned that any policy should not only be initiated but also implemented. He did not want it to be a paper exercise.

The co-ordinators were feeling that something concrete needed to happen, as well as the 'behind the scenes' talking, to raise the profile of health education in the college. They encouraged work during a Healthy Eating month, enlisting the support of the catering staff and involving students in making posters. They requested that there be stencilled 'No Smoking' notices in the lifts, as previous notices had been removed.

The college working party was formed, with all sectors of the college staff represented, i.e. support staff, students and lecturers. Recruitment was mainly by personal contact. Two meetings were held in the autumn term 1990. The first was a short, informal induction session to allow members to meet each other, to help the group to gel and to discuss the objectives of the working party. The second meeting was for a half-day. The name of the group was discussed. The majority of the group considered the term Health Education to have negative connotations and preferred to be called the Health Promotion Working Party. This also had relevance for the main business of the meeting, the discussion of the draft health policy. Working in small groups, each group considered the policy in detail, proposing amendments and changes in wording. These were discussed in the whole group and the format of a new draft was approved. There was general agreement that the policy be kept as concise and readable as possible. Under the title 'The North Cheshire College Policy Statement for Health Promotion', it has the following sections:

1. Definition of health and health promotion
2. Aims of the policy
3. Organisation
4. Staffing
5. Staff development
6. Curriculum
7. Collaboration.

The health policy was presented to the Academic Board in March 1991, and accepted with minor alterations. It will now be presented to the Board of Governors and, if accepted, will become official college policy. It is hoped to produce a handbook which will include all college policies.

The working party continued to meet, keen to see some action rather than just words. Issues which have been discussed include: offering staff and students a half-hour session to learn emergency first aid, concern over smoking in the college, opportunities for healthy eating and sport on one of the campuses, and Look After Your Heart courses for staff. A sub-group was formed to draft a smoking policy for the college.

The county working party, now known as the Health Education in FE Development Group, also continued to meet. New members from other colleges have joined as well as a representative of a local health promotion unit. The meetings offer an opportunity to share what colleges have been doing. It was decided that the colleges participating in the project would produce a report for inclusion in a county handbook and also help to deliver staff development to managers, teaching and support staff in the county.

5. Achieved outcomes

For the college
- a policy which will enhance the image of the college for clients. They also have a cross-college working party,

which is beneficial in that it is getting people together. Comments from members have been positive.

For the co-ordinators
'It's given me a wider insight into the workings of things at college and in the county. I've deliberately avoided this in the past and have never had anything to do with budgets,' was a typical comment.

Working with people cross-college gave insights into the needs of other areas.

The co-ordinators were not prepared for the amount of paperwork generated by the project, and were apprehensive initially of making mistakes: 'However, once I realised it wasn't too difficult, it was OK.' It was useful to write reports for the county, the project and to keep management informed. As a strategy, it maintained the project's profile.

Future plans

The main task is raising awareness and changing attitudes both of staff and students. Small inroads have been made, but it needs greater visibility and more than talking.

The co-ordinator is already involved in the TVEI working party and intends forging links with other areas in college (for example, NVQs) where health education could be an issue.

The Staff Development Officer is very supportive, and with his help, the co-ordinators hope to arrange relevant training.

There is some doubt about what will be possible in the future. There is no paid staff cover after the spring term 1991, although management seem very committed to continuing the work.

6. On reflection

- The co-ordinators would have preferred more time at the beginning, to think about what they were taking on and to consult with colleagues.
- The level of seniority of the co-ordinators seemed appropriate. It was important that they were interested in the initiative, not simply given the responsibility of doing it. They needed management support, but not necessarily to be senior managers themselves.

- The membership of the working party seemed effective. The co-ordinators were pleased that they had involved support staff and students, and that there was cross-college representation. There was a positive attitude and a willingness to get things done.
- The co-ordinators went through some bad patches, where it felt as if progress was slow, and they had too many conflicting priorities. They needed support and appreciated the contact with other colleges, both through the project and at county level. The meetings enhanced motivation.
- The major hindrance was a lack of money and time to put much into practice. For example, running half-hour first aid sessions for all staff needs time and resources. Given the current financial situation of most colleges, the emphasis is on raising funds. For the Development Group to continue it might need to think of ways of generating money, for instance, through a health fair.
- Health promotion needs to be visible. Policy making alone is not enough!

Contact name: Anne Hewitt   Tel: 0925 814343 x 463
Address: North Cheshire College, Fearnhead Lane, Fearnhead, Warrington, Cheshire WA2 0DB.

Northumberland College of Art and Technology

1. Background

The Northumberland College of Arts and Technology, situated on the east coast at Ashington, is the only one in a very large county and has a catchment area stretching from Newcastle to the Scottish border and some 60 miles from east to west.

Previously focused primarily on the mining industry, the college underwent great changes with the collapse of the industry and the closure of local pits. It gradually developed a broader base and now provides an extensive range of post-16 courses, both vocational and academic, for full- and part-time students.

Owing to its location and the consequent travel difficulties, the college has a hall of residence which caters for 120 students on a weekly basis. These places are supplemented as necessary by local lodgings.

Before the project there had been no tradition of providing health education for the majority of college students although it was available as part of the curriculum on specific courses, for example, Community Care.

A member of the college staff had been involved with the earlier HEA 16–19 Dissemination Project. It was felt that the Health in Further Education Project fitted in well with the new structure that the college was developing and would help to broaden the entitlement curriculum.

2. Planned outcome

- That health education would be integrated into the tutorial system and made available to all students. This linked closely with the planned introduction of TVEI extension and the requirement for a personal tutoring system.

3. Management/staffing

Originally three members of staff were involved:

- the College Counsellor, an LII/SL in Student Services, who co-ordinated the project;
- the Sector Leader for Humanities (SL) with timetabling responsibility; and
- the Head of the General Education Board of Studies.

On the restructuring of the college in September 1990 a Principal Lecturer in Student Services, who took responsibility for administration, replaced the Head of General Education and the group were joined by an SL, Head of Leisure and Recreation, who had a background in personal and social education in schools. This latter person worked closely with the College Counsellor in the delivery and evaluation of the staff development sessions.

There was no specific budget allocated but finance was provided for training and staff cover from the TVEI budget.

One hour per week each was timetabled for the College Counsellor, the Principal Lecturer in Student Services and the Head of Leisure and Recreation. This enabled regular meetings to carry through the planning and administration of the rolling staff development programme. The County Adviser for Health Education provided some of the funding for the final phase of the training.

4. What they did

Following the project residential ideas were discussed with key colleagues and two papers outlining plans for the development of health education in the college were written and presented to senior management. However, at this point the college became involved in a lengthy and somewhat stressful internal reorganisation which slowed down progress with the initiative.

Towards the end of the summer term 1990 a college working group was formed consisting of the four people mentioned above. They began designing a series of 14-hour staff development programmes to support the integration of health education into the tutorial system.

The first programme of staff development began in the autumn term 1990, with a two-hour awareness-raising/needs analysis session for the 22 participants. This set the agenda for a one-day workshop held the following week at a local hotel, and for the subsequent three two-hour follow-up sessions which took place in college.

There was an extremely positive response to the programme from most participants and their comments back at college enthused other colleagues and created a demand for places on the two programmes which followed. As some senior staff (Sector Leaders) had been involved in the initial programme they were enthusiastic about encouraging members of their sector to participate in one of the following programmes.

The second programme was run in spring 1991, with 24 staff from across the college participating. Recruitment continued for the final programme of the series, to be run in the summer term. Numbers reached 26 on this course with many other staff indicating a wish to become involved.

A typical 14-hour staff development programme

Week One	Two-hour session Icebreaker Sharing expectations Needs and wants exercise
Week Two	Whole day (6 hr) Group contract Negotiation exercise How groups work (problem-solving exercise) Action plans
Week Three	Two-hour session Raising issues Communication within groups
Week Four	Two-hour session A typical tutorial session using a thematic approach (e.g. assertiveness)
Week Five	Two-hour session Exploring themes Final evaluation and review exercise

The working group held further meetings, evaluating the success of the programmes and looking at how emerging needs, raised both by the training and by people's subsequent practical experience, might be met. It was evident that sufficient demand existed to warrant the provision of a 'second level' course.

6. Achieved outcomes

For the college
- Seventy-two members of staff engaged in the personal tutoring system have participated in the training programme and most have adopted a more student-centred approach to their teaching.
- Some more 'traditional' teachers, who attended the training with apprehension, took part enthusiastically and are now trying new approaches.

- There is a wider understanding amongst staff of broad-based health education issues.
- Members of Her Majesty's Inspectorate have been impressed by these developments and have written positive comments in their report to the college management.
- The Personal Tutoring System is on course for whole college implementation in September 1991.

For the project co-ordinator

An unexpected outcome for the College Counsellor, who co-ordinated the project, was that through building positive relationships with so many colleagues during the staff development programmes they became more willing to refer students to him for help.

He was also invited to work with groups of students on a variety of courses on the themes of group building and self-awareness.

The experience made him look again at his own teaching style and, because he expected others involved in the training to take risks, he took more himself with good effect.

There was much satisfaction from personal involvement in such a worthwhile project; specifically the experience of co-facilitating with a new and respected colleague and also receiving such positive feedback from staff.

Future plans

Although the original Health in Further Education Project has ended the college will be developing its own health education work further. Plans are already at an advanced stage to continue the programme in the coming academic year by:

- offering the initial programme until all appropriate staff have attended.
- providing a second phase of staff development to address relevant health issues raised in the first phase (for example, assertiveness, stress management).

The County Health Education Adviser has agreed to contribute towards the financial costs for the continuing training.

6. On reflection

The positive support of the senior management team has been crucial to the development and success of the project within the college. However, initial difficulties were experienced at middle management level. Some Sector Leaders seemed reluctant to release staff, believing either that the tutoring system would not happen or that it did not apply to their sector.

This reinforced for the co-ordinator the need for clear contracting in the initial stages, with perhaps an awareness-raising exercise for middle management offered prior to the launch of the training programmes.

Before embarking on the next training phase, efforts will be made to:

- secure the use of more suitable accommodation for the two-hour college-based sessions
- increase the planning time together for the co-facilitators.

Contact name: Joseph Jackson   Tel: 0670 813248 x 237
Address: Northumberland College of Art and Technology,
College Road, Ashington, Northumberland NE63 9RG.

North Warwickshire College

1. Background

North Warwickshire College, in Nuneaton, has 1500 full-time students, of whom 95 per cent are 16–20.

The following reasons were given for welcoming involvement in the project:

'Under the auspices of TVEI, a group of colleagues are planning a cross-college development of the tutorial system. This is being done with the full backing of senior management. We are especially interested in enabling students and staff to cope with transitions and in looking at stress management policies. We already have good working relationships with the local Health Promotion Unit.'

From September 1990 each student would have a one-hour tutorial. This hour would include 1:1 reviewing as well as groupwork. It was anticipated that each division would organise its tutorials differently. However, there would be guidelines laid down as to the areas they would be expected to cover and the objectives they would be expected to meet.

2. Planned outcome

- To develop student materials on stress, which could be used by tutors.

3. Management/staffing

An application form was sent direct to the Student Counsellor, as she had attended a training course as part of the previous HEA 16–19 Dissemination Project. She was interested in being involved, together with the Course Organiser for A level students. There was support for the project from the newly appointed Vice Principal in charge of student services.

Unfortunately the second co-ordinator was unable to attend the project residential because of a family bereavement. She subsequently changed to another post.

There was no remission negotiated at the beginning of the project, although this later became possible through TVEI funding.

4. What they did

In summer 1990 a working party was formed to develop student materials on stress. It consisted of six staff from different divisions. Their concern initially was that this pack could end up sitting on a shelf and not being used. How committed was management?

A meeting was arranged with the Vice Principal, to discuss the feasibility of developing the materials. She welcomed the idea, being keen to see an effective tutorial system established in the college and recognising the importance of stress prevention and management. The TVEI Co-ordinator was also supportive.

The working party decided that their first step was to research the causes of stress for students in the college. In order to devise a questionnaire, they began by asking some of their own students what had caused them stress throughout the year. At a third meeting, they discussed students' comments, for instance, the course not being as they expected, the need for self-discipline, criticism of some teaching styles, whether electives should be optional or that there should be more choice, and criticism of the toilets. A draft questionnaire was devised.

Meanwhile a new guidance unit was being established. The co-ordinator discovered that the person responsible for guidance and support was also sending out a questionnaire to all full-time students. It seemed appropriate to combine the two questionnaires. The development of materials on stress was postponed until the results of the questionnaire were available. The original group involved in this work was therefore disbanded, although most have since kept in touch and supported further developments.

In the autumn term 1990 the new tutorial system was introduced. The Vice Principal was keen to get tutorial materials together and granted three days' remission to three members of staff, funded through TVEI. The three people involved were the Student Counsellor, a lecturer in nursery nursing, who had attended the HEA 16–19 HIV/AIDS training, and a lecturer in mathematics.

It was decided that they would concentrate on writing a pack of materials on drug education, to use in tutorial time. The college had become concerned about the increasing use of cannabis amongst students and, rather than ignore the problem, resolved to confront it. The Drugs Liaison Police talked to the staff about drugs, giving basic information.

A Healthy College Group was formed, chaired by the Vice Principal. The impetus for this came from the local Health Promotion Officer. Others on the committee are interested lecturers, teaching English, PE and leisure, and nursery nursing, the Student Counsellor, the person in charge of the guidance unit and a youth worker. They are working to produce a college health policy.

The small team, who developed the tutorial materials on drug education, organised and ran staff development in spring 1991 for 15–20 staff to try out the activities in the new pack. The Vice Principal encouraged recruitment.

The materials on drugs are kept in the guidance unit.

The team are now developing materials on HIV/AIDS.

5. Achieved outcomes

For the college

The college has materials to support drug education and a team to offer consultancy and team-teaching as tutors require.

A process has been established for developing health education materials.

The team itself had benefited from developing links with people outside their own division.

The Healthy College Group has been established to draw up a policy statement and decide priorities for action.

For the co-ordinator

It was good to work with others in a different context from counselling. She had wanted to be involved with groups of staff and in her role as college counsellor was also keen to help prevent some of the problems which students present.

Future plans

In order to support tutors using the materials, it is hoped that one of the four people who helped in their development will be available to offer support and team-teach. However, time could be a problem if they are in great demand.

Further staff development is planned to introduce people to the pack on HIV/AIDS.

Possibilities for future materials include: Sexuality and gender, Stress and Assertion.

6. On reflection

- The co-ordinator did not have the support of a colleague at the project residential course. With hindsight she considers that one person cannot do the work alone. A team is needed. The work carried out in college would have been impossible without the commitment of a number of interested staff, from a range of backgrounds.

- It was also crucial to have the support of the Vice Principal.
- The introduction of an hour's tutorial for all students offered an opportunity for health education.
- Similarly the money available through TVEI made it possible for staff to get remission to develop materials.
- Although there was close contact with the project consultant during the summer term, this faded from September onwards. According to the co-ordinator it helped to know that there was someone available at the end of the phone, but support within the college meant that she did not need to turn to outside help. Similarly, her heavy workload influenced her decision not to attend the last two-day meetings of colleges involved in the project.
- The workload of other members of staff also created difficulties. Staff interested in health tend to be interested in other issues such as equal opportunities. Most have multiple responsibilities. This situation was worsening as the college was faced with losing up to 60 staff, following poll tax capping. The work was non-stop, with the college taking on board issues such as modularisation, flexible learning and access funds.
- It would have been preferable to have negotiated remission at the beginning of the project.
- It has taken longer than perhaps initially envisaged. It will be over a year before staff involved see the fruits of their work.

Contact name: Liz Shaw   Tel: 0203 349321 x 2160
Address: North Warwickshire College of Technology and Art, Hinckley Road, Nuneaton, Warwickshire CV10 6BH.

Otley College of Agriculture and Horticulture

1. Background

Otley College of Agriculture and Horticulture was opened at its present site 21 years ago and was extended in 1988 when the nearby Farm Training Centre at Chadacre was incorporated. Situated in the heart of rural Suffolk Otley College caters for approximately 1000 students per week drawn from throughout the county. The postgraduate courses in conservation and management attract students nationwide. Owing to its location, travel to the college can be difficult and a residential hostel provides termly accommodation for up to 50 students. This is supplemented by lodgings in the surrounding small villages.

Several of the specific vocational courses have included elements of health education in the syllabus – for example, Environmental Protection, Health and Safety, and Management of Harmful Substances (learning how to use agricultural chemicals without damage to yourself or others).

The project was welcomed as a means of introducing health more widely across the whole college and moving from a curriculum focus towards a student-centred approach. However, the person responsible for the development of personal and social education within the college left soon after the project's inception. This effectively deprived the initiative of an overall management figure.

The Special Needs Department at Otley, although initially small, seemed to be a rapidly growing area with numbers increasing by over 50 per cent during the one-year time span of the project. This made it an ideal area in which to start the initiative.

2. Planned outcomes

- To raise awareness of student-centred health education throughout the college
- To provide continuing support for interested tutors
- To create a central resource area for health education materials
- To compile a list of available county resources.

3. Management/staffing

The two people allocated responsibility for the project were an LII with a full teaching timetable within the special needs section of the college and an LI, new to the college, with a full teaching timetable and also 'warden' responsibilities at the student hostel.

The Professional Development Officer for the county was very supportive and allocated a budget of £1200 to provide cover for attendance at the project residential course, follow-up day workshops, design and analysis of a questionnaire and report writing.

4. What they did

Initially in the summer term 1990 links were formed with the Curriculum Development Group who, under the auspices of TVEI, were considering 'enhancement' of student learning through the introduction of a tutoring and guidance system throughout the college.

A tutoring guide was produced to encourage and support staff interested in becoming tutors and several staff development sessions were run. Together with the TVEI Co-ordinator, the project leader was involved in the planning and delivery of the staff development.

During the two-week induction period in September 1990 health education was introduced by the project co-ordinators to several of the new student groups. These were mainly 'one off' sessions with National Certificate courses, designed to raise student awareness and encourage thought about their individual health education needs.

With the special needs students, practically based sessions on diet related to the students' own financial situation were used to generate the agenda for the term. In this way health education topics became integrated into the curriculum for these student groups.

Following the successful completion of the staff handbook, attention during the autumn term was focused closely on student needs. A handbook explaining the purpose and organisation of the tutoring and guidance system was designed for distribution to all students. It was hoped to have this printed ready for the start of the new academic year in September 1991.

To support all these developments the college counselling service was augmented by additional staff attending local training courses.

As more people became interested in the project a list was compiled of people with relevant health education expertise who were willing to support their colleagues by co-teaching specific sessions. In this way all students would have access to a wider range of health topics.

In March 1991 a questionnaire was sent to all teaching and support staff within the college. The purpose of the questionnaire was:

- to find out what aspects of health education were already being covered;
- to seek staff views on what health topics should be covered; and
- to ascertain whether they favoured cross-college provision or integration into the course curriculum.

The results of the exercise were rather disappointing, with only 25 people (25 per cent) returning their complete or part completed forms. However, the returned questionnaires did highlight some positive trends:

(a)   Health issues which are directly relevant to vocational courses are already well integrated into the curriculum.

(b)   Staff are in favour of a wide range of additional health topics being made available to their students. (More research is needed in order to clarify staff views on the best way to provide for this.)

(c)   Strong support was recorded for the inclusion of the following health issues in the college provision: HIV/AIDS, Stress and relaxation, Alcohol and drugs.

(d)   Use of the questionnaire raised the profile of health education in the college and established that there is a foundation of practice to build upon.

5. Achieved outcomes

- Greater awareness of health education amongst staff and genuine enthusiasm from some colleagues.
- Health education has a higher profile within the college management system.
- The college now has a core group of tutors willing to offer certain elements of health education to support their colleagues.

Future plans

Based on the analysed results of the questionnaire, they hope to provide staff development for tutors that will encourage and support future health education work.

They are at present working to build stronger links with the local health authority in order to involve them in continuing health education developments within the college.

Being a highly vocational college with a strong emphasis on training perhaps there is a greater need to open out the training *v.* education debate to encourage a broader view.

6. On reflection

Looking back over the period of the project the following changes might have enabled more progress with the initiative.

- Owing to college reorganisation and the introduction of Local Management of Colleges there appeared to be a lack of stability and security amongst staff which inhibited the adoption of a more pro-active approach to the project. This raises questions about the timing of the project.
- Clearer and more specific goals from the outset might have helped. It became obvious that the initial objectives were too ambitious.
- Definite and committed support from key people within the college needed to be clarified before the project began.

Contact name: Jonathan Price   Tel: 0473 785543
Address: Otley College of Agriculture and Horticulture, Otley, Ipswich IP6 9EY.

Redbridge College of Further Education

1. Background

Redbridge College, situated in North East London, was built in the 1960s and has 900 full-time students with a total full- and part-time enrolment of 6000. It is a multi-cultural college with 50 per cent of the full-time enrolment of Asian origin. The predominant work of the college is that of general education and vocational courses, co-ordinated by 13 Programme Team Leaders. The catchment area and practice of Redbridge College covers four London boroughs: Redbridge, Newham, Barking and Waltham Forest.

Previous work has included health education within some of the vocational courses, in particular the caring courses and nursery nursing.

Within the college student community centre specific college events related to health education have been organised, for example, Drinkwise Day, No Smoking Day and information/ awareness sessions on HIV and AIDS.

Individual tutors have used the resources of the local health education department to enhance current curriculum content.

Good contact exists between the college and the local health education authority and the Redbridge Drug Education Project.

The Welfare Officer has done much to promote health education and through counselling has gained a sense of student needs in relation to health education. She also has good contact with local health education bodies.

The college chose to be involved with this project in order to produce a more coherent approach to health education within the college.

2. Planned outcomes

- To link with, and learn from, other colleges
- To work towards ensuring that health education becomes part of what the college is offering as part of the entitlement curriculum, by encouraging the development of student-centred learning and supporting health education activities during students' tutorials
- To form a learning and development group of staff members from throughout the college to raise awareness and build confidence in using health education processes of learning.

3. Management/staffing

Overall responsibility for the project rested with the Education Support Tutor, who was responsible to the Assistant Principal (Student Services), and a lecturer with an interest in and experience of student-centred approaches. In addition, a Programme Team Leader responsible for Caring, Health and Beauty courses has been linked with the project to help realise outcomes.

No specific time release has been given to the project as its co-ordination is seen to be part of the remitted time of the Education Support Tutor. No time release has been given to the lecturer involved.

Finance to support the project is available through the Learning Resources Centre and from the central administration budget. Specific bids have to be made to support proposed initiatives. During the course of the project funds have been found to enable the two project staff to attend the national residential and training days and to fund a day's training for 15 members of staff, including costs for cover.

4. What they did

Following the attendance by the two staff members at the residential course, there was a greater awareness of health education issues and processes. The opportunity to learn from and network with other colleges enabled the staff members to be clearer about what it was possible to achieve within the college and to feel supported in their action. Out of the residential course emerged the production of an action-plan based on the planned outcomes, already described.

This has led to increased liaison with local health agencies such as the Health Promotion and Drugs Education Co-ordinators. This resource is now more widely recognised within the college.

A proposal was drafted to form a learning and development group from staff members and to develop health education processes as part of the entitlement curriculum. This was submitted to the college Academic Board and received approval. It led to access to funds and use of the college structures to develop the initiative.

A training day at Redbridge Teachers' Centre was organised for core members of the learning and development group. It covered such topics as relationship building and communication skills, working with change and learning styles. It enabled the tutors to gain practice in the use of health education materials and processes and laid the foundation for further work and support.

On the whole the project staff have used existing committee structures within the college and the support of the Assistant Principal (Student Services) has been crucial in this process as he has been able to gain access through the senior management team to the Academic Board. The initiative to create a learning and development group of staff was a deliberate attempt to break down some of the barriers between the various programmes within the college, and to encourage horizontal support and networking. The support given by the Education Support Tutor to staff was an important element in the process, as her role enabled her to ensure a regular flow of information to tutors and the provision of specific material for tutorials, for instance, on stress and study skills. She enabled staff to build up confidence in the materials and processes and was there to support staff in taking risks to develop their work and styles.

In order to undertake the above, it was and will continue to be necessary to involve the following: senior management, personal and course tutors, Programme Team Leaders, the college Welfare Officer, the local health education team and the borough TVEI team.

5. Achieved outcomes

For the college

It was provided with outside training, which highlighted the need to develop tutorial provision both to adopt and to make explicit an entitlement curriculum. It provided a focus for informed debate about college goals for student-centred learning.

For the co-ordinators

There has been much personal learning, initially to be open to the concept of health education, and then a significant outcome was a greater emphasis on using the process approach within teaching. Both members of staff felt more confident in dealing both with health education issues and with a wider range of teaching/learning styles, for example, being prepared to undertake a choice-orientated curriculum in their tutorials that had been negotiated with their students. They also gained knowledge about organisational change.

Future plans

The project staff would like to build on this initiative to create a tradition of activities related to health education, so that they become part of the college culture. New styles of learning that go beyond the existing few courses and tutorials would be developed so that support for students would be embedded into teaching and tutorial practice.

Substantial teaching resources would be developed and held in an accessible and well-known location. These materials would be used for both vocational courses and entitlement activity in general.

A bid has been made for a whole college staff training day on health education and its processes, to take place at the end of the summer 1991 term. This would consolidate the work already carried out and would form the basis of staff training in relation to general tutorial activity.

Much of this work could be incorporated into a college Quality Development Project that would involve a wider range of staff from within the college.

It is intended to maintain and develop links with Health Promotion and Drug Education Co-ordinators, to make them more widely available throughout the college.

6. On reflection

- The residential course was particularly useful: firstly being away from college, it allowed attention to focus entirely on health education without any distractions and secondly much was gained from the other course participants, especially in terms of college initiatives, systems for bringing about change and other related developments in education, for instance, Records of Achievement.

- Back at college, away from the enthusiasm and commitment of the residential course, there was the learning to cope with the frustration of indifference, slowness of change and the inability to remain constantly motivated. This could be counteracted next time by doing things differently. The action-plan would be more rigidly adhered to, others would be involved from the beginning of the project, ideas would be taken to senior management and specific times extracted from them for achieving identified goals. Remission for discussion, planning and consultancy would be negotiated in advance and progress records would be maintained.

The project staff found the spaced training days helpful, as these provided both support and momentum. They also found it helpful having a specific trainer and consultant allocated to the college. This gave continuity and being external to the college permitted demands to be made and helped clarification of roles and relationships.

The major hindrances to the development of the project centred around the difficulty of engaging staff interest. Many staff are interested in learning styles, student-centred approaches and making their tutorials more interesting and relevant, but are put off by the term health education. Because of the constant new initiatives that are taking place it is difficult to find time for health education and there was, and continues to be, a lack of time to engage in planning, reflection and evaluation both for project staff and for staff generally. It is important that health education, if it is to be meaningful for both staff and student, is linked to wider developments and processes taking place in further education.

Contact name: Cherril Wilson   Tel: 081-599 5231 x 261
Address: Redbridge College of Further Education,
Wittle Heath, Romford Essex RM6 4XT.

Richmond-upon-Thames Tertiary College

1. Background

The college has, approximately, 3240 full-time students mainly between 16 and 19, with equal numbers male and female. The student population is mainly middle class but includes students from a variety of backgrounds.

The college had been part of the HEA 16–19 Dissemination Project. At that time health education issues were promoted by a small group of enthusiasts. There was a desire to broaden the approach by developing a whole college policy on health promotion. It was thought work could be done on grouped and mainstream courses. At the same time thinking would continue around the personal and social education issue.

2. Planned outcomes

- To set up a working party with members from all areas of the college: teaching, non-teaching, administrative and support. The working party would aim to meet the following objectives:

  (a) Development of a health-promoting college and the promotion of the concept of the college as a healthy environment;
  (b) Raising of awareness of health issues amongst all students and staff and the encouragement of maximum involvement in the implementation of a health policy;
  (c) Investigation of the opportunities for and the development of health education within the core entitlement;
  (d) Encouragement of student ownership and responsibility for health issues within the college;
  (e) Ensuring maximum use of the expertise of outside agencies, including link schools, in the development of the college health policy.

3. Management/staffing

One co-ordinator had a background of CPVE and science, the other CPVE and pastoral. One of the co-ordinators prepared a bid for the Vice Principal and the Chief Administrative Officer seeking: remission from class contact from September 1990 of two hours a week for the two co-ordinators; administrative support of one person for four hours a week; and £500 for materials, photocopying and resources. Under the Local Education Authority Training Grants Scheme, a bid was submitted for £1000 to cover staff development and interviews. This was provided from LEA funds.

Overall responsibility for the project lay with the college working party, chaired by the Director of Student Services. The project linked in to core entitlement and student support.

4. What they did

The first residential course held by the project enabled the two co-ordinators to talk to colleagues from other colleges and to work with each other to plan a strategy.

A working party was formed of sixteen staff. A paper describing the project and objectives for the college was submitted to the Academic Board and Governors.

A range of tasks was agreed by the working party. The allocation of resources to allow for detailed documentation of the college's project was agreed and the working party's progress reported to Governors and to the Academic Board. Listed below are the tasks which were agreed and what actually happened.

The collation of all existing policies in the borough relating to health: The LEA Advisory Teacher for Personal, Social and Health Education and the Health Promotion Officer supplied copies of borough policies on HIV/AIDS, World Health 2000, Action on Alcohol and Smoking in the Workplace, together with results of surveys carried out by them in the borough.

A survey of staff to collect information on those interested in contributing to health education/core entitlement: Questionnaires were circulated and lecturers were canvassed directly. A staff development session was run for interested staff. It was seen as an awareness-raising session with a focus on ideas for practice.

The canvassing of students' opinions and perceptions of health education/health policy by means of consultation with the Students' Union: Questionnaires were circulated to 500 students: 8 groups per faculty.

The investigation of the role of Junction 3, the project run by youth workers in the college: The college nurse and a youth worker from Junction 3 agreed to co-ordinate an event linked to No Smoking Day on 13 March. Work was carried out with a group of BTEC students from health and care courses to arrange activities. Students have formed a Smoking Awareness Group.

The development of resources and teaching materials: In the end, the project decided not to focus on this, as help and advice were available from a range of sources.

The investigation of health needs/issues as perceived by the college nurse/doctor: The college nurse agreed to keep a record of issues/problems brought to her by students in a similar way to the counselling staff. She also records accidents reported in the college. She has provided information sheets to staff on diabetes, glandular fever, and epilepsy.

A survey of the environment of the college in collaboration with the Health and Safety Committee in the light of new regulations: Following a report from the representative of the Health and Safety Committee, the working party agreed to ask for a review of health and safety in the college.

A survey of current issues in personal, social and health education in borough schools: The two co-ordinators met representatives of the borough Phase Panel with a view to building on the work done on personal and social education in schools.

The development of a health education input to the college's core entitlement for September 1991: A senior lecturer co-ordinated the health education input into the core curriculum. During 1990/91 it was a pilot programme run as a six-week block. In the pilot students devised their own schemes of work. The issues they identified as important were: stress, HIV/AIDS, health and diet, and alternative medicine.

Evaluation of the courses will feed into future planning. Long term it seems core skills will be delivered through the mainstream curriculum. A college working group has been set up to plan it.

Restructuring in the college led to a reorganisation of the tutoring system. The opportunity for the delivery of health education through the pastoral curriculum diminished.

An interest was expressed in college smoking policies. One of the co-ordinators gave the Vice Principal a proposal for developing and implementing a college policy. This was accepted by the management group and a member of staff has been asked to co-ordinate it.

5. Achieved outcomes

The outcomes for the college are listed in the previous section.

For the co-ordinators
- the opportunity to put into action some of the ideas about health education that we think are important and to move things along in college. However, we have also learnt not to be over-ambitious in trying to overcome the inertia in institutions.
- a feeling of being in places where things are happening and to get ideas for innovations, although while imagination is needed to see what can be done, reflection on what is happening is important.
- enhanced appreciation of planning skills and appreciating each other's skills and recognition of how they are complementary.
- an understanding of the people skills involved in bringing about change and a recognition that change is a continuous process.

For the working party
- the outcome for members of the working party has been an increased awareness of the work that has been done across the college in health education and the potential for work in future, together with knowledge of some of the work that has been going on in the other case study colleges.

Future plans

- A college smoking policy will be implemented.
- The working party will continue after the project.

- It is hoped to provide effective health education across the college.

6. On reflection

- The fact that the two co-ordinators were from different faculties was an advantage, widening their network in college. They were both recognised as confident, experienced people involved in curriculum development.
- There was continual pressure owing to lack of time. The promotion of both of the co-ordinators gave them extra work as well as that of maintaining the momentum of the project. However, their support for each other was vital, and they are committed to the belief that they need to be in the mainstream to influence change.
- Previous involvement with the HEA 16–19 Dissemination Project was an asset, working with previous contacts, building on what had gone before, and feeling part of a wider movement.
- The working party played a key role in the work of the project. The support of the chair, the discipline of reporting progress to the working party and regular meetings, drew all the threads together. All the members provided ideas and suggestions and played an active role in the work. It would have been useful to include BTEC Health students on the working party.
- Regarding the structure of the project, the co-ordinators found it valuable to attend the meetings with the representatives from the other case study colleges and also appreciated the involvement of the project consultant.
- The core skills debate came at an opportune time to review provision for 16- to 19-year-olds.
- It was important to have support from the LEA and the continuing interest of the Advisory Teacher for Personal, Social and Health Education (now Inspector for TVEI). On the other hand, personnel changes meant certain posts were unfilled during the life of the project, for example, the Health Promotion Officer

moved to another district: she had been a constant
support to the college.

- Another time the co-ordinators would try to identify the
benefits for staff of becoming involved in the project and
doing more for their personal health.

Contact name: Kathleen Wildman   Tel: 081-892 6656 x 3488
Address: Richmond-upon-Thames Tertiary College,
Egerton Road, Twickenham, Middlesex TW2 7SJ.

Sandwell College of Further and Higher Education

1. Background

Sandwell College is situated on the edge of the Black Country.
It was amalgamated in 1985 with West Bromwich College of
Technology and has six campuses across the borough. The
college has about 2000 full-time and 18 000 part-time students
annually. There are 1000 academic and support staff.

Sandwell was at the heart of the heavy engineering industry
in the Black Country. Owing to the economic recession large
numbers of people have become unemployed. The college has
responded to this with various retraining courses and also
sponsorship from successful companies.

An awareness of changing client needs and recognition of
how environmental factors affect our lives led to the
appointment of a Health Education Co-ordinator on a senior
lecturer grade. The role of the officer is to co-ordinate health
education across the curriculum and to raise staff and student
awareness about health education.

The post started in April 1989. There were eleven such 'link-
up' posts within the college aiming to make provision across all
the sites for such things as marketing, publicity, school links,
BTEC, access, etc, and now health. The co-ordinator
appointment was on a half a timetable, 'eighteen-hour SL' basis,
giving only nine hours teaching each week leaving the
remaining time free for health education duties. She was
responsible to the Vice Principal and reported directly to him.
The co-ordinator had previously been involved in national and

local health education events, for example, Drinkwise and AIDS
awareness. She had also organised 'Health Discos' for the new
student intake and set up a health education resource base.
The main aim of the resource base was to supply help and
information on health to all members of staff and students and
to provide teaching materials. The new post was seen by the
newly appointed officer as an opportunity to promote health
awareness to the staff that would have a cascade effect on the
students and would also provide the opportunity to link with
similar people in other parts of the country.

2. Planned outcomes

- To set up a system of staff training workshops in which
  'positive health' in the curriculum is explored in an
  exciting and innovative way
- To enable members of staff to approach 'positive health'
  issues confidently in their class time
- To use and build on resources already available in
  college and to look at their 'worth'
- To introduce a system of continuing help/support for
  staff involved in presenting 'positive health' issues.

3. Management/staffing

College management was supportive throughout the project.
Two hours' remission was given to the co-ordinator and to a
staff member who offered to become involved to help with work
on the project. Later, owing to increased duties, both workers
were unable to take the remission time. Initially finance was a
problem as it was unclear from which budget the money should
come. Once finance was organised the workers were given a
free hand as to its use, which meant that projects they were
planning could go ahead.

4. What they did

The main aim of the project was to raise awareness so that
further training could take place and so that staff would have
the confidence and knowledge to address health education
issues.

A working party was set up to generate ideas and see if practical help was forthcoming. Despite there being representation from all areas of the college the response from the academic staff was poor. However, the support staff put forward several ideas, such as a staff health club that would include fitness testing and exercise. The working party decided that there would be no further value in continuing without the support of academic staff, and it was therefore dissolved.

A Health Fayre week was held in February 1991. A specially equipped truck, with leaflets, posters and videos on health, toured the college campuses. This roadshow was intended as an awareness-raising exercise for both staff and students. Computers were also available for participants to obtain feedback on their lifestyle, such as drinking, eating and smoking. These were particularly popular.

Additionally, twelve staff from each campus were given health and fitness tests by the local health promotion unit brought into the college. A cross-section of staff was tested in private and given computer printouts suggesting relevant lifestyle plans. This was popular and it has been requested that it be repeated.

The following contributed to the fayre's success: the release of money by the Vice Principal and a free hand in its use, plus the combined support and practical help of the college marketing manager, technicians, computer manager, campus managers, security staff, lecturing staff and college management in general. This highlights the need to establish good relationships and communication throughout the college if such an event is to have any impact. However, if numbers = success, it was not totally successful on every campus, despite much advertising.

The national and internal changes to college organisation during the project's lifetime were a hindrance. The Vice Principal was one of forty people who took early retirement and, despite support from the Principal and other Vice Principals, the day-to-day running of the project was more difficult and delays occurred with his departure, as there was no direct line management support.

During the internal reorganisation of the college when thirteen departments were split into thirty-four schools, pressures on staff were increased, making it difficult to call on the staff for help and support. In addition, increased responsibilities and a heavier workload for the project staff caused further delays to the project.

Because of her involvement with senior management, the co-ordinator was invited to give a presentation on the project to the Board of Governors and was invited to present the project's outcomes to the newly established Human Resources Committee, a subcommittee of the Board of Governors.

5. Achieved outcomes

- Health awareness among college staff has grown and more health education training has been requested.
- Another outcome is a slimming club on campus!

Future plans

Staff training sessions have been arranged and it is hoped from these to set up a network of interested staff.

It is hoped that the project will act as a springboard for future events and training. As staff become more aware of the need to take an active part in their own health it is hoped that this will be transmitted into an increased recognition of responsibility towards their students. The aim is to provide training for staff both in the raising of awareness and in the delivery of health education throughout the curriculum.

It is also hoped to establish closer links with other colleges enabling the sharing of ideas and resources.

It is hoped that health education will be seen as an integral part of the curriculum and not as an extra. The entitlement curriculum and the care curriculum as well as quality initiatives can be enhanced by health education approaches and processes.

From September a 'window' has been made on a Wednesday afternoon for student involvement in a wide range of activities. One of these is a health club which, it is hoped, will lead to a personal level of student involvement in health.

6. On reflection

- The project staff felt that both they and the college benefited from the project. They themselves benefited from the external network with whom they liaised and appreciated the goodwill and support of others, both within and outside the college.

- The kudos of being involved in a national project gave more 'weight' to a management already committed to health education.
- Involvement and support from senior management and regular contact with them is essential for their understanding of the project.
- The co-ordinator found that the seniority of the position and her involvement with other college committees, and also committees linked with the district health service and the health promotion service, gave her an advantage in gaining support and provided a useful network of people.
- It is important to 'think big' and not see our health as a side issue in the curriculum. Thinking big may not achieve all the aims but it does raise the profile of health issues.
- The need for networking was a real learning experience; many working in the health education field are often working in isolation. The setting up of support both within and outside the organisation is essential. Both workers recognise that in setting up a project there is a need for help from others. Both were disappointed at the failure of the original working party and wonder if they should have delegated more responsibility earlier on. However, within an atmosphere of so much internal change this would have been difficult.

Contact name: Lesley Boyden   Tel: 021-556 6000 x 8218
Address: Sandwell College of Further and Higher Education, Kendrick Campus, Kendrick Street, Wednesbury, West Midlands WS10 9ER.

South East Derbyshire College

1. Background

The college has 2400 full-time equivalent students, of whom there are 1700 full-time and 3000 part-time. Students are drawn mainly from the surrounding small towns and are largely white, working/middle class. Significant programmes in Business Administration and A levels are in operation and an expanding number of caring courses are offered.

Through links with what was happening county-wide in Derbyshire, an enthusiasm for health education began to grow amongst a small number of staff at the college. However, lack of an appropriate structure and support system for health education made it difficult for them to bring back and implement the new ideas.

There were several health-related courses running in the college and this is mainly where enthusiastic staff were able to channel and try out some of the new approaches. (For example, the full-time BTEC National Diploma in Caring Services has included assignment work on stress management.)

With the introduction of the new college structure a Student Services Section was created, which had as part of its remit responsibility to encourage the personal development aspect of the curriculum. The Head of Student Services decided to adopt a dynamic approach, in essence to be pro-active in fusing and channelling the enthusiasm which already existed in staff; finding a way of marrying this with the college structure and its priorities; and identifying small concrete steps for development.

It also seemed important to maintain a strong contact with the Derbyshire Health in Further Education Group, which provided a positive focus for future development.

2. Planned outcomes

- Working with young people to create health education materials for their age group and others
- Developing policies, for example, on alcohol and smoking
- Developing a health workshop as a resource and activity centre
- Relating health to overall curriculum entitlement, and the reviewing process for students.

3. Management/staffing

The Director of Student Services, appointed as Head of Department grade IV, became involved in the project as he saw it as a definite part of his role. He took responsibility for the overall co-ordination of the initiative, including the writing of reports for senior management and the Academic Board. A lecturer in caring from the General Education and Applied Social Science programme area, on a full teaching timetable, became his fellow co-ordinator. She worked without any contact remission from the project's inception in March 1990 until the end of the summer term July 1990.

In the new academic year September 1990 until July 1991, two one-and-a-half hour secondments (teaching abatements) were offered. These secondments were allocated to the lecturer in caring, who had been involved with the initiative from the beginning, and a further lecturer in special needs.

A specific budget was provided for the initiative from Grants for Education Support and Training funds. The County Advisory Service covered all the expenses for the two co-ordinators to attend the project residential course and the additional follow-up days. During the spring term 1991 small amounts of supplementary funding were drawn from the Student Services and TVEI budgets.

4. What they did

On returning from the project residential course the Director of Student Services spent time writing a report for the Academic Board in order to raise awareness of health education within the college. This coincided with the distribution of Derbyshire County Council's guidelines to colleges – the Council was preparing a policy document on health education. In response to this document the Director of Student Services wrote a Health Education Policy Statement for the college, which was agreed by the college management team at their next meeting in June 1990.

The lecturer in caring devoted much time to talking to people, trying to raise interest in health education and to enlist the support of her colleagues. She researched various packs and resources to identify appropriate activities which might be useful in the introduction of health education, via the induction programme, in the following September.

The two secondees met in October to discuss health education issues and priorities at the college. They specifically highlighted smoking and stress management as areas for awareness raising and policy development. Together with the Director of Student Services they began researching ways of implementing a smoking policy for the college.

One way of reaching a wide audience within the college was through the library provision. Meetings were held with the librarians at both college sites to explore the possibilities for displaying health education leaflets and books to increase awareness of specific topics. The idea of setting up a 'health shop' within each library was also explored. In spring 1991 health education materials were identified and displayed in the college libraries. These have been well used by students.

Another development which was planned during the autumn was the design of three ten-week, health-related courses, for inclusion in the personal development programme offered through the electives afternoon. It was suggested that these ideas should be discussed by the College Health Education Co-ordinating Committee, when it was established.

In the spring term 1991 an advertisement was placed in the college newsletter inviting people to join this committee. The following volunteers were sought: 'one representative from each section of the teaching staff, one tutor per centre and one representative of support staff'. The committee was formed with eight members and conducted its first meeting in March 1991. The project workers were able to seek support with the continuing development of the various initiatives.

The smoking debate was launched and the proposed policy was considered by the new committee at each stage, with the specific target of creating the structures to support implementation by December 1991.

The committee was also actively involved in discussions about the inclusion of health education within the tutorial curriculum and in the design of a proposed Health Week.

5. Achieved outcomes

For the college
- a college policy on health education, which is linked to the county policy. This has been accepted by both the senior management team and the Academic Board. It was essential for this to be in place to provide the necessary support for implementation. The policy gives not only the authority but also the obligation to act on it (i.e. the policy statement now requires action as a recognised part of people's jobs).
- a support system is now in place which responds to health education issues raised by students.
- through the links which already existed the co-ordinators have kept the college counsellor informed of developments in health education.
- a cross-college Health Education Co-ordinating Committee has been established, now with ten members. This committee will meet twice each term to support health-related events and to continue the development of ideas.
- some students have identified specific health education needs through the tutorial system, and have had these met by the provision of additional short courses, for example, Assertiveness for Women was provided in response to a request from secretarial students.

For the project co-ordinators
- the opportunity for professional development through cross-college activity and discussion.
- the chance to extend health education issues beyond their immediate teaching areas.

Future plans

The Health Education Co-ordinating Committee's efforts will culminate in much activity during the following few months. Amongst the plans are:

- A *Health Week* which will be held in mid-April.

- Preparation for the Derbyshire *Theatre in Education* production on the issues of HIV/AIDS.
- Continued development of a college *smoking policy* using the ASH pack and other resources.
- To plan and prepare an *induction programme* for new students entering the college.
- To offer *health modules* within the electives programme, as part of the personal development commitment. The aim is to make health education high profile, accessible and negotiable, avoiding any suggestion of it being compulsory or imposed.
- To explore further the links between health education and TVEI.

6. On reflection

The project co-ordinator felt that essentially he would tackle any new initiative in the same way. That is, by making sure that all the structures and helpful mechanisms are in place within the college before attempting to initiate anything with staff and students. However, he did think that it might have been effective to try to give more responsibility to the other staff involved in the project. As the Director of Student Services he had many responsibilities and it was often difficult to give priority to the project. In any future project he would be more realistic about the amount of time he could give and would delegate responsibility sooner.

Perhaps greater efforts could be made to 'connect' with other current developments in post-16 education, especially those which are a national priority, in order to increase the number of opportunities (for example, the current core skills debate).

The opportunity to become part of the Health in Further Education Project certainly enabled the college to force health education to a higher point on its agenda.

Contact name: Robin Goddard   Tel: 0602 324212 x 301
Address: South East Derbyshire College, Field Road, Ilkeston, Derbyshire DE7 5RS.

Stockport College of Further and Higher Education

1. Background

This large college had a total of 14 300 students, of which 4620 were full-time. There was a wide age range, with 40 per cent 19 years old or under.

Over the preceding twelve to eighteen months, staff were faced with major changes. The internal structure changed with, amongst others, departments merging and heads being re-located. Agencies were created with cross-college functions, such as a curriculum development agency. There were also changes in procedure, for example, new forms to be filled in. A new Principal had recently been appointed.

With the appointment of a Head of Student Services, support for students was seen as an area for further development. The college was interested in being involved in the project in order to explore stress management for staff and students. Better provision in this area was one of their priorities.

2. Planned outcomes

- To examine the degree of stress experienced by staff and students
- To propose methods and models that could be implemented to reduce the stress levels
- To gain acceptance for the introduction of a stress management policy with college-wide commitment to its success.

3. Management/staffing

Funding arrangements and time for the work were clearly thought out from the start. The college guaranteed to release two members of staff, each for one day per week from April to December 1990, to carry out the work in college. In addition they would pay for attendance and travel to the project workshops. A bid for £3500 was approved by the LEA, from the Local Education Authority Training Grants Scheme, to cover this.

The project was supervised by the Head of Student Services. A steering committee was set up, to receive progress and final reports and to consider the feasibility of implementing any recommendations made. Its membership comprised the Senior Adviser, Further Education, the Head of Student Services, the Project Consultant, the two co-ordinators and the Vice Principal.

4. What they did

Their starting point was to undertake three activities:

- to involve as many people in the college as possible
- to review the copious literature on stress
- to plan a realistic approach.

For various reasons, not least the time of year, they decided to begin their study with the staff.

The two co-ordinators wrote to all heads of faculty asking for their support in naming two staff from their faculty who would be willing and interested in being involved in a college working party to explore staff stress. They gave details of what this would involve, that is, attendance at four meetings, two each term, and distributing and collecting questionnaires.

A college working party was formed with representation from administration, support staff and each faculty. The members agreed to talk informally with their colleagues about the type of stress experienced in their section of the college and what they felt created it. This was then fed into the first meeting and helped in devising the first draft of a questionnaire for all staff.

Concurrently they reviewed literature on stress, looking in particular for books which offered help, insight and experience in viewing stress as an organisational issue as well as a personal problem. One book was particularly helpful: *Stress Management*, by Deborah Clarke (National Extension College, 1989).

The final design of the questionnaire was the result of ideas taken from the literature, the issues raised by the working party and the advice of the steering committee. It was distributed to every full-time member of staff. In all 524 questionnaires were distributed. Responses were collected in by the working party. The co-ordinators then analysed the 228 returns (a 43 per cent response).

In October the results were discussed at a meeting of the working party. Each member was given the first 12 introductory pages of the 100-page report, together with the section relating to their faculty. There was general agreement that it had been a worthwhile exercise. It was decided that the co-ordinators would write a précis of the report and the working party would suggest recommendations. In the end few recommendations were received. The general impression seemed to be that the working party had 'done its bit'.

In November the steering group, including the Principal, met to discuss the report and possible ways forward. Staff needed to know that this was not just a paper exercise. It was decided that the next step was to give all full-time staff a copy of the short report, with the information that the senior management team was considering the implications for them of this survey.

Meanwhile the co-ordinators were asked to find out whether any other college had carried out similar work.

The co-ordinators met the senior management team in spring 1991 to discuss the findings and the way forward.

As part of the process of learning from the experience of other colleges, they visited Solihull College, which over the last four years had been changing its way of working, and communicated with Preston College, which had used an outside consultant to examine stress-related issues.

5. Achieved outcomes

For the college
- Stress as an issue has been recognised, but there is a danger that it will be dealt with in a piecemeal fashion, or left to the Principal.
- There is a possible strategy identified to deal with stress.
- It has been shown that issues can be raised on the shop floor and brought to the attention of senior management.
- It has increased cross-college awareness of the college climate, the similarities of issues in different departments and the special difficulties in certain areas.

- Certain sections have seen immediate benefits and improvements, for example, the porters now have the trolleys they wanted.
- Some initiatives will have an immediate effect. These include the improvement of the fabric of the building, the appointment of security staff and surgeries where the Principal listens to the concerns of a school.

For the co-ordinators

It has increased their profile in the college. They feel a little like representatives of the college, which is empowering but also a responsibility.

They recognise more fully the formal and informal networks of the college.

It has given them insight into the senior management team and the pressures which they are under. It has also led to confirmation of where the power and decision making lies.

Future plans

- The co-ordinators intend to present their findings to the senior management team, offering suggestions for the way forward. These will include dealing with stress themselves, bringing in a consultant, and leaving it alone!
- It seems likely that the college will form a 'task force' to deal with the issue, in conjunction with an outside consultant.
- Some initiatives, for example, concerning quality management and college procedures, will have a long-term effect, it is hoped.

6. On reflection

- The co-ordinators would amend the questionnaire, if they were using it again. Certain questions were not clear.
- With regard to the distribution of the questionnaire, many staff were uneasy at returning answers to a third person, a member of the working party who worked in the same faculty. It was difficult to maintain anonymity.

More thought could have been given to confidentiality.

- Computer processing of the material would have both speeded up the analysis and made the findings more statistically rigorous.
- They would have kept the working party going, for continued support. They tended to feel rather alone with the task as the work progressed.
- The workshops organised by the project were useful, but not of direct application to their task. No other college was working along similar lines, so that the national support network was not very effective.
- There should have been more rigid time parameters. Once the survey had been carried out, the project seemed to drag on without a clear sense of direction.
- Given the scale of response and the detail offered by respondents, the co-ordinators felt that the findings from the survey constituted a valid and clear picture of stress as experienced by staff in the college.

Contact name: Peter Smith   Tel: 061-480 7331
Address: Stockport College of Further and Higher Education, Wellington Road South, Stockport, SK1 3UQ.

References

Abbott, J. and Gee, L. (1989) 'Fitness – why and what are we testing?', *Health Education Journal*, **48** (1), 14–16

ASH (1988) *How to Achieve a Smoking Policy at Work*. Action on Smoking and Health (ASH). (Based on the Fourth Report of the Independent Scientific Committee on Smoking and Health [the Froggatt Report], HMSO, 1988)

Beattie, A. (1980) 'A structural repertoire of the model of health education', Health Education Certificate Tutors' Workshop, Exeter, March 1980

Beattie, A. (1986) 'Community development for health: from practice to theory?', *Radical Health Promotion*, issue 4

Charlton, A. (1983) 'Clues to planning smoking education for the sixteen-plus age group on vocational courses', *Health Education Journal*, **42** (3), 71–3

Deere, M. (1992) 'Lessons from the first year', Speech to the Recording Achievement and Higher Education Project Dissemination Conference, Birmingham, 25 June

DES/LAA (1987) *Managing Colleges Efficiently*. HMSO

DES (1987) 'Providing for quality', *DES Circular* 3/87, May

DES (1989) 'Local Education Authority Training Grants Scheme: financial year 1990–91', *DES Circular* 20/89, August (See also Grants for Education Support and Training, DES, for the years 1991, 1992 and 1993)

DES (1991) *Education and Training for the 21st Century*. 2 vols. Cm 1536. HMSO

DH (1991) *Dietary Reference Values for Food Energy and Nutrients for the United Kingdom*. A Report of the Panel on Dietary Reference Values of the Committee on Medical Aspects of Food Policy. HMSO

DH (1992) *The Health of the Nation: a Strategy for England*, White Paper, Cm 1986. HMSO

Dhillon, H. S. and Tolsma, D. W. (1991) *Meeting Global Health Challenges*. A position paper on health education at XIV World Conference on Health Education, Helsinki, Finland

FEU (1989) *Towards a Framework for Curriculum Entitlement*. Further Education Unit

Goldblatt, P. (1989) 'Mortality by social class 1971–85', *Population Trends*, No. 56, 28 June

Gray, G. and Hill, H. (1993) *Health Action Pack: Health Education for 16–19s*. HEA, 2nd edn

Handy, C. (1989) *Age of Unreason*. Hutchinson

Health Education Authority/Sports Council (1992) *Allied Dunbar National Fitness Survey Main Findings*. HEA/Sports Council.

Health Education Authority (1992). *Today's Young Adults* (Report on the survey period March–May 1990) : 16-19 year olds look at diet, alcohol, smoking, drugs and sexual behaviour. HEA

Health Education Authority (1993) *HIV/AIDS Education in Six Colleges*. HIV/AIDS Sexual Health Paper. HEA

Hill, F. and Turner, G. (1993) *Health Education Authority 16–19 HIV/AIDS Project – HIV/AIDS Education in Six Colleges*

Jackson, E., Neate, D. and Walshaw, J. C. (1984) *Physical Education in Further Education – the Need for a Systematic Approach to Curriculum Development* (FEU Occasional Paper). Further Education Unit

Jee, M. and Reason, L. (1988) *Action on Stress at Work*. HEA

MAFF (1989) *Food Safety: Protecting the Consumer*, White Paper, Cm 732. HMSO

National Curriculum Council (1990) *Curriculum Guidance 5: Health Education*. National Curriculum Council, York

OPCS (1991) *Smoking among Secondary School Children in 1990*. Enquiry by Social Survey Division of OPCS on behalf of Department of Health, Welsh Office and Scottish Home and Health Department. HMSO

Peters, T. J. and Waterman, R. H. (1982) *In Search of Excellence*. Harper & Row

Public Health Laboratory Service (PHLS) (1992) *Communicable Disease Report Weekly*, **2** (30), July (Communicable Disease Surveillance Centre)

Rawson, D. and Grigg, C. (1988) *Purpose and Practice in Health Education – the Training and Development Needs of Health Education Officers*. Summary report of the SHER Project, Southbank Health Education Research (SHER). Polytechnic of the South Bank

Ryder, J. and Campbell, L. (1988) *Balancing Acts in Personal, Social and Health Education*. Routledge

Townsend, P. and Davidson, N. eds (1982) *Inequalities in Health: the Black Report*. Penguin

Whitehead, M. (1987) *The Health Divide: Inequalities in Health in the 1980s*. Health Education Council (See also Townsend, P. and Davidson, N. eds and Whitehead, M. (1988) *Inequalities in Health: 'The Black Report' and 'The Health Divide'*. Penguin)

WHO (1978) *Primary Health Care*. Report of the International Conference on Primary Health Care, Alma-Ata [Declaration of Alma-Ata]. WHO, Geneva. (See also WHO (1985) *Targets for Health for All: Targets in Support of the European Regional Strategy for Health for All*. WHO Regional Office for Europe, Copenhagen; and Faculty of Community Medicine of the Royal College of Physicians of the UK (1986) *Health for All by the Year 2000, Charter for Action*)

WHO (1984) 'Health promotion', supplement to *Europe News*, No. 3, 1984